MR. WILLIAM JAROSZEWSKI
2123 West Roger St.
South Bend, Indiana 46628

D1364957

MASERS AND LASERS

How They Work, What They Do

M. BROTHERTON, Ph.D.

 McGRAW-HILL BOOK COMPANY

New York   Toronto   London

MASERS AND LASERS

II

08124

Dedicated to the scientists who work to discover
and explain the underlying principles of our
physical world and to the engineers who develop
ways to apply them for the good of all

FOREWORD

Tools, inventions, and technology have always been crucial to the species known as man. And gradually with developing technology has come a systematic knowledge and understanding called science, which is not only important to man's view of himself and his surroundings but which has allowed more complex and subtle tools of civilization to be developed at an ever-increasing rate. Science and technology may now be counted along with "bread" as basic to man's material sustenance. Yet at the same time, science has become sufficiently complex and subtle to be continually in danger of being estranged from the society it serves and by which it in turn must be nourished.

The wheel and the arch could be touched, examined, or made by any individual, and an understanding of their uses developed over many generations. The latest inventions today are frequently based on great abstractions, they may involve atomic phenomena never really visible to or touchable by anyone, and millions of people may experience their effects and benefits within a short time after discovery.

The maser, with its variant the laser, represents such an invention rooted in abstract atomic and quantum theory. To the quantum scientist, the theory involved is beautiful, and the device fascinatingly powerful in allowing control of radiant energy in the form of electromagnetic waves. But others who do not deal with quantum physics in an everyday way are usually separated from such appreciation by a frustrating chasm; the theory is likely to seem unreal, and the maser itself a most mystifying and fantastic device. This book is designed to show the nonspecialist, by relatively simple steps understandable to the interested mind, how the theory and the device developed, what the maser is and how it works, and the beauty and power of the resulting complete structure.

Brotherton's discussion is a happy combination of an easy and interesting style with anecdote, history, and analogy, careful attention to the significance of each major step, and much closer adherence to scientific reality than is usually achieved in simplified or popular discussions of complex scientific ideas.

His association with the Bell Telephone Laboratories and with its scientists, who have been closely connected with much of the story of the maser, has given him an excellent vantage point from which to produce such a treatment. But also evident is his enthusiasm for an accurate and understandable presentation of exciting science and its applications.

This type of writing is much needed in order to prevent the estrangement of science and scientists from the broader public, and it must be read if this public is to profit best from the enormous potential of science or to remain in sentient control of its own destiny.

C. H. Townes

PREFACE

This book began in 1960 when I was working on a Bell Laboratories advertisement on the maser. I became so intrigued with the device itself and how it worked that I went on to put what I had learned into an article entitled, "Amplifying with Atoms." Published in the *Bell Laboratories Record,* the article proved of such wide interest among science teachers, science students, writers, and others that it was necessary to provide nearly 30,000 reprints.

These events revealed a lively need for science writing in such a vein and at such a level of understanding, and this book developed virtually as a response to that need. In it I have tried to portray the laser and maser against their common generic background, explaining in an elementary way how they came to be, how they work, how they can benefit science, technology, and communications, and how, in general, they provide an intriguing insight into the workings of nature.

Since the book is intended to communicate only key ideas, all illustrations are made as simple as possible and stylized as necessary, consistent with accuracy. Names of persons, except historical ones, are omitted to simplify the narrative and to avoid invidious omissions.

This book was conceived for that considerable audience of literate people both here and abroad who would like to have an explanation of masers and lasers which, while factual and authentic, stays away from formulas and formulations beyond their grasp.

Written in spare moments during evenings, holidays, and weekends, at home, on park benches, and on commuter trains, this book is a purely personal project. The viewpoint expressed is my own and does not necessarily represent that of Bell Telephone Laboratories. Surely, however, it could not have been written without the perceptive comments and guidance and, by no means least, the sympathetic interest and encouragement of several members of the Bell Laboratories technical staff. Particularly, I want to acknowledge the help of D. F. Nelson, A. N. Holden, J. N. Shive, J. E. Geusic, E. F. Vaage, and D. C. Hogg; also that of Professor C. H. Townes, of Massachusetts Institute of Technology, for guiding me to information sources.

I am indebted to articles in *Scientific American*. For possible uses of these devices, I have consulted the report of a study entitled "Masers and Lasers," prepared by graduates of Harvard University Graduate School of Business Administration. Information about why the laser was not invented earlier was found in a thesis prepared by Michael Feld for Massachusetts Institute of Technology. Finally, I must acknowledge my indebtedness to Bell Telephone Laboratories for the use of its facilities and for permission to publish most of the illustrations.

M. Brotherton

CONTENTS

Chapter 1. ELECTRICITY, MAGNETISM, AND WAVES   9

The laser as a new type of electromagnetic-wave generator utilizing the same elementary forces of electricity and magnetism as do other generators · How these forces interact to produce electromagnetic waves · How electromagnetic waves were discovered · The electromagnetic spectrum

Chapter 2. ELECTRONS AND ELECTRON TUBES . . 23

Laser radiation originates in electrons · What the electron is like · How electrons like those in lasers work in wires for electric power and telephony · How they work *in vacuo* in electron tubes to generate and amplify · The frequency limitations of triodes and klystrons

nessed · The application of a magnetic field for tuning · Some
benefits derived from microwave technology

The first laser · Solution of the resonance problem by means of
parallel mirrors · The production of laser action in the ruby by
harnessing the activity of orbital electron-magnets · How two gases,
caused to work in partnership, made possible the first laser able to
produce a continuous beam

The semiconductor-junction laser · Discussion of electrical conductivity in insulators, conductors, and semiconductors · How the p-n
junction arises in the union of p and n semiconductors · How the
junction which gives rise to the transistor and solar cell also produces laser action · Some advantages of the junction laser

What we need to know about waves to appreciate masers and
lasers · All sound, radio, light, and all communications depend inevitably on wave action · How wave motions add to form complex
patterns while the individual rhythms continue to be distinguishable · Fourier's theorem · The sine wave or frequency as the "atom"
of the world of vibration

The comparative outputs of wave generators, natural or man-
made · The wide continuous frequency band of incandescent solids
versus the spectral lines of hot vapors · Radio transmitters produce
single "spectral lines" · The radio transmitter's wave output is coherent · Why the laser's output is, at the same time, intense, coherent, and extremely directional · Laser light compared with sunlight

How masers can be used to advantage in spectroscopy and time
measurement and as low-noise amplifiers in the reception of weak

signals in satellite communications · Discussion of reasons for vanishingly small internal noise in the ruby traveling-wave maser

INTRODUCTION

One day in 1954 a Columbia University professor and his students startled the world of science by generating radio waves without using the customary electron tube. They generated these waves (which are about one-half inch long and known in electronics as *microwaves*) in a small metal box which contained nothing but a small quantity of ammonia gas differing chemically in no way from the household cleanser you pick up in the chain store. Instead of drawing upon the energy of a stream of electrons as was done in all earlier types of radio-wave generators as far back as Hertz's pioneer radio experiments in 1887, they produced microwaves by stimulating the emission of energy which was stored in the ammonia molecules. Fittingly these pioneer Columbia University scientists named their device *maser,* which is short for *m*icrowave *a*mplification by *s*timulated *e*mission of *r*adiation.

As a practical tool of communication the maser may never compete with other less complex microwave amplifiers, which it is able to outclass in only one important particular. The significance of the discovery lay in the radically new amplifying principle it revealed. Dramatically, it drew attention to an exciting vista of possibilities for harnessing atoms and molecules to store and manipulate radiant energy both as tools for probing matter and in practical devices. In numerous universities and industrial concerns physicists began looking for ways to apply the new principle at shorter wavelengths and with different materials and techniques.

By 1959, the operating frequency had been thrust upward through the electromagnetic spectrum a hundred thousandfold to create the *optical maser,* or *laser,* capable of working with light waves only a tiny fraction of an inch in length. Essentially a laser [1] consists of an active medium which may be a crystal, gas, or semiconductor. It is bounded on two ends by parallel mirrors which reflect light waves back and forth. The atoms of the medium through which the

[1] Some prefer the term *optical maser,* in which the letter m is made to stand for *molecular* instead of its originally assigned denotation of *microwave*. While this viewpoint is logical, we shall here employ the word *laser,* since it has the virtue of brevity and has won popular acceptance.

light waves are reflected are conditioned to give off light when light hits them. As the light waves race to and fro, they release new energy from the atoms and are thus amplified. By making one of the end mirrors partially transparent, the amplified light is caused to emerge as a beam.

The laser achieves the historical distinction of being the first device capable of amplifying light waves per se. This may seem strange when we consider that we have had excellent radio-wave amplifiers for many years and that light waves are of exactly the same electromagnetic nature as radio waves, differing from them only in wavelength and frequency. What is there about the laser that enables it to handle light waves while other amplifiers cannot?

One factor is that the laser handles and amplifies waves as waves without having to convert them into a vibration of electrons as was necessary in earlier amplifiers. Paradoxically, the three-element electron tube, which more than any other invention made possible our fabulous world of radio, is quite incapable of handling radio waves as such, that is, as vibrations in "empty" space. Strangely enough, the only part of a radio receiver that actually handles radio waves is the antenna. Scooping radio-wave energy out of space, the antenna converts it into vibrations of electrons in wires, and it is these vibrations which the electron tube handles and amplifies. By its very nature the three-element tube is incapable of operating at extremely high frequencies. Consequently, for more than a generation, with no other amplifier available, communications science was hampered in its quest for higher frequencies.

Then in 1938 came a new kind of electron tube called the *klystron,* and in 1946 the traveling-wave tube in which waves interact directly with an amplifying electron stream. Eliminating the necessity for having to convert the waves into vibrations in a wire circuit, the klystron and traveling-wave tube can handle enormously higher frequencies, that is, shorter wavelengths, than the earlier tubes.

Great as are the advances made possible by the klystron and traveling-wave principles in handling short wavelengths, still they are incapable of operating at the extremely short wavelengths of light mainly because physical parts cannot be made small enough or electrons made to move fast enough. By creating a situation in which light waves amplify themselves by drawing directly upon energy stored in atoms, the laser takes a giant leap over both obstacles, opening the way for the manipulation and application of light waves in ways never before possible. Broadly the applications fall into three categories.

1. For pure science, the laser principle offers a new and useful point of view from which to study the behavior of matter, while the light itself affords a new and potent source for spec-

troscopic studies. Extremely intense, sharply focusable, and virtually single-frequency, the laser
beam offers a means to trigger chemical reactions and to explore molecular structure.

2. In the fabrication of mechanical parts the laser
beam can be focused to provide intensities never
before attainable, which can be applied to cut,
punch, and weld without the part having to be
touched.

3. In communications—the conveyance of meaningful signals—the laser has twofold promise.
In radar, it can be used to detect objects and, in
general, smaller details of objects than can be
done with microwaves. In telephone, television,
and data transmission, laser beams can theoretically provide superhighways for communication.

The notion of employing light for voice communications is not novel. As far back as 1880—only five
years after the invention of the telephone—Alexander
Graham Bell set up an experiment which demonstrated the feasibility of transmitting a voice by light
waves over a distance of several hundred feet. Also,
light beams have long been used to imprint sounds
as tracks on movie film, then to convert the tracks
back into sound as we listen. The great new thing
about laser beams which so stirs the imagination of
communications scientists is that they are theoretically capable of transmitting voice and TV programs

—all at once—in enormously greater numbers than can be carried by present-day radio beams even when the latter are employed to their utmost capacity.

What may turn out to be one of the most significant consequences of the advent of the laser has been its promotion of a vigorous, creative interaction between the optical and radio disciplines. Because of the widely different uses to which optical and radio waves have been put in science and industry and the widely different techniques and instrumentation through which they are handled, the optical and radio disciplines have been thought of in different contexts. The new interaction between the disciplines may lead to developments of a power and brilliance that cannot be foretold.

How did the basic principle which makes possible all masers and lasers (the *aser* principle, so to speak) come to be thought of? Unlike other great but also notably unpremeditated advances in the history of science and technology, the discovery of the aser principle was no accident. In this respect it is unlike the telephone, which was accidentally invented by Alexander Graham Bell while he was seeking to develop a new kind of telegraph; or the emission of electricity by hot wires (the central phenomenon of all electron tubes), which was stumbled on by Thomas A. Edison as he worked on his invention of the electric lamp; or X rays, which turned up quite unexpectedly when Roentgen found that photographic plates lying on a bench in his laboratory were mysteriously blackened. In contrast, each of the pioneer masers and lasers was deduced from theory ahead of its embodiment in a physical device; each illustrates both the startling capabilities of our fundamental physical theory and what the enterprising and imaginative mind can achieve in applying these esoteric theories in practical ways.

Then, too, the discovery of the aser principle points up a significant new trend in electronic science and technology. More and more we are having to penetrate into, and to understand, the inner nature of materials in order to make new advances. In the beginnings of our electrical era during the last century, an inventor could invent without knowing the inner nature of what he was dealing with. Morse's telegraph, Bell's telephone, and Edison's electric lamp did not require that their inventors know the nature of electric current. In contrast, the transistor was invented by men who had as profound an understanding as had anyone else at the time of the behavior of electric charges within the precisely patterned interior of semiconducting crystals. Then, too, in the field of nuclear science it is hard to see how atomic power could have been realized without a prior theory of nuclear fission. In sum, in the accidental type of advance you first discover something new, then figure out what you've found. The maser and laser exemplify a more modern approach in which you first figure out what must be, then go into the laboratory and prove it.

Surprisingly, perhaps, the physical phenomena behind the aser principle were known to physics for many years before its advent. For example, the idea that atoms could be stimulated to emit radiation had been proposed by Einstein in 1917, and the fact that atoms can be caused to store and emit radiant energy at microwave frequencies (and for that matter at a near-infinite number of other frequencies as well) had been known to spectroscopists for many years. With all this known, why did the first maser not appear upon the scene until 1954?

Probably we can never know exactly why a scientific advance comes into being at a particular time and in a particular place, but we do know that it must wait until the essential ingredients are brought into creative interaction in somebody's mind. There are three basic ingredients in all masers and lasers—three major keys to their action—regardless of the operating wavelengths, the materials used, or the outward forms of the device. It was by bringing them together for the first time that the Columbia University scientists created the first maser. Let us see the nature of the three keys and how they came to be known and applied.

1 | ELECTRICITY, MAGNETISM, AND WAVES

The laser as a new type of electromagnetic-wave generator utilizing the same elementary forces of electricity and magnetism as do other generators · How these forces interact to produce electromagnetic waves · How electromagnetic waves were discovered · The electromagnetic spectrum

Essentially, the laser is a new type of electromagnetic-wave generator. As such it joins a varied list of man-made wave generators, including flames, electric lamps, neon and fluorescent lights, and X-ray generators as well as the wave generators of radar systems, radio and TV stations, and an even more varied list of natural generators like the sun, aurora borealis, lightning, fireflies, and phosphorescent fish. No matter how different these wave generators may appear, all utilize the same fundamental forces of electricity and magnetism. To develop an understanding of lasers, let us begin by reminding ourselves of some of the elementary properties of electricity and magnetism.

Consider first an electric charge (which may be either positive or negative) perched in "empty" space. It is surrounded by an electric field, a region in which there exists a force capable of moving another electric charge, repelling one of like sign or attracting one of opposite sign.

Let us now suppose that we cause this electric charge to move in a circle. The moving charge becomes a current of electricity, producing around the path of its motion a magnetic field in which there exists a force capable of moving a magnetic object such as a compass needle, either attracting or repelling the north pole (let us say) of the needle, depending on the direction of rotation of the charge. This phenomenon also works in reverse. A magnetic field made to move across a stationary charge sets the charge in motion, thus generating electric current. If now we go a step further and make the electric charge oscillate, its electric and magnetic fields will oscillate in unison. Under particular conditions, energy is radiated into space as electromagnetic waves (Figure 1).

To establish a perspective in which to view the laser and other wave generators, let us first briefly recall how electromagnetic radiation came to be discovered. This takes us back to the middle of the eighteenth century.

Even at that time experimenters with electricity had long known that an electrically insulated metal plate possesses the ability to store an electric charge. In 1745, P. Van Musschenbroek of the University of Leyden in Holland demonstrated that when two insulated metal plates are brought into close proximity without touching, the combination is capable of storing, or "condensing," enormously more charge than could be held by a single plate. The *Leyden jar,* as the device was named, has the distinction of being the original ancestor of today's condenser, or capacitor.

When a wire is connected to one plate of an electrically charged Leyden jar and then made to touch the other plate, there is an electrical discharge which may be extremely violent (when the voltage is high). We could give some cold figures as to the amount of electricity stored, but the idea is far better conveyed in an account of an experiment by a certain J. H. Winckler in Leipzig in 1775.[1]

> . . . the first time he tried the Leyden experiment, he found great convulsions by it in his body; and that it put his blood into great agitation; so, that he was afraid of an ardent fever, and was obliged to use refrigerating medicines. He also felt a heaviness in his head, as if a stone lay upon it. Twice, he says it gave him a bleeding at his nose to which he was not inclined. His wife received the shock twice, and found herself so weak, that she could hardly walk; and a week after, upon recovering courage to receive another shock, she bled at the nose after taking it only once.

Those of us who have accidentally touched a charged high-voltage capacitor or been shocked by a spark plug will readily sympathize with Mr. and Mrs.

[1] Joseph Priestley, *The History and Present State of Electricity,* 3d ed., London, 1775, vol. 1, p. 107.

Winckler as they reached for the refrigerating medicine.

Other investigators found that they could kill small birds with the discharge from a Leyden jar and used the discovery to entertain the ladies of the French court. Benjamin Franklin made the gruesome observation that he could kill a chicken by connecting Leyden jars in *cascade;* he also tried to kill a turkey, but the native bird proved too tough. Then there was the celebrated experiment in which Franklin lofted a kite in thunderous skies and anchored the kite string to a Leyden jar. With characteristic prudence he then withdrew to await the result. On returning, he found the jar electrically charged, indicating that lightning is electrically caused.

Though the invention encouraged experiments with electricity, and much was learned about the characteristics of condensers and the conditions under which they work best, there was no inkling as to the tremendous possibilities that lay hidden in the spectacular sparks. These possibilities would indeed continue to lie hidden until the middle of the nineteenth century.

At this time—more than a quarter of a century before the word *electron* would be coined—little more had been learned about the fundamental nature of electricity than in Franklin's day. However, a great deal had been learned about the properties of electricity in motion. Around 1786, some 40 years after the invention of the condenser, the Italian physiologist Galvani had made the celebrated discovery that a frog's leg muscles twitch when the frog is suspended by dissimilar metals maintained in contact. Following this and other clues to the generation of electricity by chemical action, the Italian physicist Volta suspended copper and zinc plates in an acid solution to produce the first operating battery—the first device to generate a steady flow of electric current. This was a tremendous advance, for now, instead of having to work with electric charge produced by friction and precariously perched in a condenser, experimenters could work with a steadily flowing electric current.

It was while experimenting with a current in a wire that Oersted, some 20 years later, discovered that the current produced a magnetic field around the wire. Thus, the relationship between electricity and magnetism, long conjectured, was experimentally established. Soon thereafter, Ampère, Henry, and Faraday went on to unravel and establish the laws by which the interaction between magnetic fields and electric currents is governed.

In 1853 the Scottish physicist Lord Kelvin performed a calculation which nicely illustrates how theory can reveal facts that escape the experimenter. At that time the laws of electromagnetism were well known, having indeed already been put to practical use in Morse's telegraph, and they were well on their way to application in the electric power generator. With so much known about the magnetic action of electric current we may wonder that no one envisioned the possibility of electromagnetic waves.

Setting up and solving equations to express the electric and magnetic conditions involved in the discharge of a condenser, Kelvin made the crucial discovery that in certain circumstances the electric charge must vibrate like a twanged banjo string. During the fleeting fraction of a second of the discharge, the current must pulse back and forth many thousands of times between the two plates. With the current doing work against electric resistance, all the energy must be dissipated as heat. The introduction of the concept of the oscillating electric circuit—later to become a key to all radio transmission—at once set the stage for another and even more far-reaching scientific advance.

In 1864, the Scottish mathematical physicist Maxwell deduced that not all the pulsating energy in Kelvin's oscillator dissipates as heat—some of it must radiate into space as waves of electromagnetic energy. He went on to develop and perfect that extraordinary intellectual feat, his theory of electromagnetic waves.

Nearly a quarter of a century later in 1887—eight years after Maxwell's death—Heinrich Hertz of Leipzig experimentally confirmed Maxwell's prediction by generating electric oscillations that actually radiated waves into space. He also proved that the waves could be reflected, refracted, and polarized just like light.

Thus, Maxwell and Hertz established beyond doubt the electromagnetic nature of light. Today we know that radio, light, infrared, ultraviolet, X rays, gamma rays, and cosmic rays all belong to one immense family.

As shown in Figure 1 a train of electromagnetic waves consists (in its simplest form) of a vibrating electric field moving through space and accompanied by a vibrating magnetic field. We note that there are three basic ways in which such wave trains may differ. First, they may differ in strength (the amplitude of

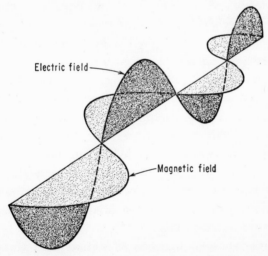

FIG. 1 Electromagnetic waves consist of a vibrating electric field perpendicular to a vibrating magnetic field. The waves shown are polarized, vibrating in two planes only.

the swing), that is, in the intensity of the electric and magnetic forces. Second, they may differ in frequency, which is the number of times they vibrate (the number of complete cycles they perform) in each second. Third, they may also differ in wavelength, which is the distance between their crests or troughs (the distance in which they execute a complete cycle of motion).

If we assume that all waves travel at a single velocity (which in a vacuum is the speed of light), a little arithmetic shows that frequency is inversely proportional to wavelength; waves of longer lengths have lower frequencies, and vice versa. It also follows that frequency and wavelength are two equally valid ways of characterising waves.

In Figure 2 we display the immense range of the electromagnetic spectrum in terms of both frequency and its inverse partner wavelength. Roughly the spectrum is divisible into two domains, each of which has been the proprietory interest (so to speak) of notably different disciplines, and each of which has its own preferred jargon. While the upper domain has been explored by physical science, especially by atom scientists and spectroscopists, the lower one has been the particular concern of communications science and engineering.

Physicists tend to think of radiation in terms of wavelength; they speak of angstroms (a hundred-millionth of a centimeter), of microns (a millionth of a meter), and millimicrons as well as of a unit called a *wave number* (the inverse of the frequency). Meanwhile, communications engineers prefer to think in terms of frequency; they speak of cycles, kilocycles, megacycles, gigacycles, teracycles, and megamegacycles. In a book such as this which involves both domains and is at the same time intended for the general reader, who is probably not on comfortable terms with all these units, it appears desirable to employ as few different units as are absolutely necessary. To avoid our having to stop to recall the differences be-

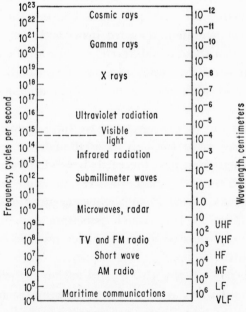

FIG. 2 The electromagnetic spectrum.

tween such things as gigacycles and kilocycles or angstroms and wave numbers, we shall (with some exceptions) specify frequency in terms of cycles per second (cps) and wavelength in terms of centimeters. Where large numbers are involved, we shall employ powers of 10: thus 1,000,000 is succinctly expressible as 10^6, and $\frac{1}{1,000,000}$ as 10^{-6}.

Referring again to Figure 2, we see that the electromagnetic spectrum extends from a frequency of 30,-000 cps, corresponding to a wavelength of 10^6 centimeters (over 6 miles), to a frequency of 3×10^{22} cps and a wavelength 10^{-12} centimeter. It is to be wondered at that the only differences between the waves of the spectrum lie in their frequency and wavelength, and yet that these two differences make all the difference in what the waves can do to our bodies and senses, and what we can make them do for us in technology.

At the top of the spectrum we have cosmic rays, which pass right through us as though we weren't there, then deep into the earth beyond. Descending the spectrum to lower frequencies, we come next to gamma rays, which in sufficient concentrations have fatal effects; X rays, which penetrate our flesh to shadow our insides; and ultraviolet rays, which tan our skins.

Next there is the visible-light region, which may appear relatively narrow when we consider its importance to us as living creatures—it stimulates the plant growth by which we are directly or indirectly fed, and through it we perceive the form, color, and texture of our world. Next we come to infrared, which we sense as heat, and beyond to the relatively unexplored and unexploited submillimeter region, which we shall refer to later. At still longer wavelengths reside all the waves that have (so far) been successfully harnessed for communications.

All this radiation, widely though it varies in wavelength and frequency, has a common origin: it all originates in moving electric charges which may be positive or negative and may arise in a multitude of different ways involving different atomic or molecular action. In lasers, as in electrical communications, the electric charge with which we are principally concerned is a negative one: the electron. We consider it in the next chapter.

2 | ELECTRONS AND ELECTRON TUBES

*Laser radiation originates in electrons ·
What the electron is like · How electrons
like those in lasers work in wires for electric power and telephony · How they work
in vacuo in electron tubes to generate
and amplify · The frequency limitations
of triodes and klystrons*

It could be argued that our progress in electrical communications stems from the development of new ways of making use of electron activity. This was surely true of those cardinal advances, the triode, klystron, and traveling-wave tube—and it is undoubtedly true of the laser.

Electrons themselves do not change, only the manner in which they are employed. The electrons that work in lasers are like the electrons that work in wires for electric power and telephony and like the electrons that race through the airless space of electron tubes in radio or TV. Indeed, from an electron's "point of view," wires, electron tubes, and lasers may seem to differ only in the environment in which the electron operates and the manner in which its energy is applied.

Now, we shall glance at how electrons work in wires, then at how they perform in electron tubes. After that we shall go on to observe the electron at work in atoms and then in lasers. But, first, a word as to the electron itself.

Since we are having so much to say about the electron, we should like to be able to say what it is or, at any rate, what it is like. The electron (except for a small amount of mass) is pure electricity, and is probably not like anything at all that we can see in our everyday life. Even if we magnified an electron to the size of a baseball, we do not know what we would see, or whether we would see it at all. Contrarily, though, we have a very good idea of what the electron does; indeed no other entity of the unseeable world has an existence or character that is better established by both theory and experiment.

We know, for example, that the electron is the ultimate indivisible unit of negative electric charge. It is also one of the smallest things in existence. An electron is so small that, even if we could magnify it 5 million times, it would still be no larger than a speck of dust. Electrons are also exceedingly numerous. Sir Arthur Eddington once estimated the number of atoms in the universe at the inconceivably immense figure of 1 followed by 76 zeros; since electrons are components of atoms, their number must be even greater. We know, too, that in the temperate conditions of our planet these infinitesimal packages of negative electricity exist chiefly "in captivity" in atoms, where they appear as the satellites of a dominant central nucleus which is positively charged.

Later we shall see how captive electrons work in lasers, but for the moment we are concerned with certain electrons that break away from their atoms (particularly in metals) and are at liberty to move about. It is to these movable electrons that the phenomenon of electric current in wires is due.

In most substances the electrons are firmly anchored in atoms and are not movable except under electric forces of destructive magnitude. In contrast, an electrically conductive substance such as copper has a great number of electrons which are not attached to atoms; they are readily movable.

As a conductor of electric current a wire behaves like a long thin pipe in which is imprisoned a gigantic number of free electrons. Agitated by heat energy and mutual repulsion, the free electrons dart hither and thither, in every conceivable direction, like a swarm of flies in a hot kitchen. Each constitutes an electric current accompanied by its inevitable magnetic field; but since there are likely to be just as many electrons moving in any particular direction as in the opposite direction, the net current and the net magnetic field are zero (which is why a piece of copper seems electrically and magnetically dead, even though it is chock full of billions of minute electric currents and magnets).

To put these one-electron currents to work for us, to produce a usable electric current, we must impose on them an ordered motion. This is possible, first, because the electrons are free to move and, second, because the number of electrons the "pipe" can accommodate is strictly regulated. If we attempt to add electrons in any region of the pipe, that is, to increase the concentration, the presiding forces instantly act to push the excess into the neighboring regions. Conversely, a decrease in concentration at any point causes an inrush of electrons to make up the deficiency.

One way to change the concentration of electrons is to connect the wire to the terminals of a battery. Through chemical action the battery produces an excess of electrons at the negative terminal, an excess which the battery will get rid of at the slightest opportunity. So, when we connect the wire between the terminals, electrons are instantly pushed into the wire. Adjusting to the repulsive force exerted by the newcomers, the electrons at the near end of the wire instantly bunch up and move over to make room. This region of the wire now has more electrons than it can tolerate; to correct the situation, the wire pushes the excess along to the far end. Here the wire is connected to the battery's positive terminal, which maintains a deficiency of electrons and will accept the excess. With the negative terminal pushing electrons into the wire and the positive terminal pulling them out, a current of electrons is kept steadily flowing along the wire.

We note that the production of electric current is

not like pouring water into an empty pipe; rather it is like pushing water into a pipe that is already full of water. To carry current a substance must naturally contain movable electrons; to produce electric current we must make electrons which are already present move over. We see, however, that an electron can never move rapidly along a wire; it can move no more than a minute fraction of an inch before meeting interference from other electrons. What, then, is it that travels so fast in an electric circuit?

No condition of balance in nature is more vigorously guarded than that of the free electrons in a copper wire; it is instantly responsive to the slightest disturbance. Suppose we briefly switch the battery on and off, thus applying an unbalancing pulse of voltage to the wire. Like a puff of wind rippling across a wheat field, the pulse is transmitted to the far end of the wire, at nearly the speed of light. Thus, the wire provides a superbly sensitive medium for transmitting pulses of electromagnetic energy.

In principle, the wire may be used to carry informing signals or to carry electric power. For either case there has to be a way to push electrons. In the telegraph, we push with a battery, interrupting the current by means of an on-off key, to send Morse code. Power transmission employs a radically different pushing technique.

We saw that electric currents and magnetic fields work in a reciprocal partnership. Just as an electric current generates a magnetic field, so a magnetic field made to move across a wire generates current in the wire. This reciprocal action is put to work in the electric power generator. A wire coil is caused to spin around its axis between the poles of an electromagnet. As the coil cuts across the field, magnetic force reaches into the wire, grips the electrons, and sets them in motion around the coil. However, at each half turn the direction of the magnetic field through the coil reverses and, consequently, so does the current. Thus, as the coil rotates (usually 60 times a second), the current surges to and fro in unison, transmitting pulses of electromagnetic energy over outgoing wires.

Greatly simplified, this is how electric power is generated and sent to our homes. Here, the powerful alternating surges of electromagnetic energy may be led into a coil in an electric motor where they rotate an armature, which in turn may rotate the hands of an electric clock or work a washing machine. Or, the electromagnetic energy may flow into a heating unit, where, working against electric resistance, it heats a toaster or lights a lamp.

In its use of electrons in wires, telephone service is akin to electric power service. When you pick up your telephone to make a call, you switch on a battery which applies pressure to the electrons in the wire connecting you to your party. As you talk into the transmitter, the sound waves (actually waves of air pressure) make a diaphragm vibrate in unison with them. The diaphragm changes the air-pressure vibrations into corresponding mechanical vibrations. In turn, the diaphragm (by varying the electric resistance) makes the pressure on the electrons vary accordingly. Corresponding pulses of electromagnetic energy speed through the electron population along the wire to the receiver. Here the pulses seize control of an electromagnet located in your party's receiver; reaching out magnetically they compel a diaphragm to move in unison, which action in turn reproduces the original sound waves.

In the elementary telephone circuit as in the telegraph and electric power transmission that we have described, the action takes place in a wire—a solid substance. In 1873, came the crucial hint that an electric charge does not necessarily require a solid substance in which to travel; given suitable conditions, it can travel in empty space.

From the days when Queen Elizabeth's renowned physician, Doctor Gilbert, entertained Her Majesty with original experiments in electricity, then on through the invention of the Leyden jar and Franklin's kite experiment, through the discovery of the laws of electromagnetism and their practical application in the telegraph, and almost up to the invention of the telephone, the only known way to conduct an electric charge was by providing a pathway for it through an electrically conductive substance, usually a metal.

Then, in 1873, F. Guthrie observed that a charged electroscope gradually discharged when it was placed near a heated ball, although there was no physical contact whatsoever between them. A cold ball had no effect; but when the ball was heated, it apparently produced an emanation which traveled to the electroscope across the intervening space. In the 1880s, J. Elster and H. Geitel, and T. Edison, went on to discover that an electric current flowed from a hot filament, across a vacuum, to a metallic plate, the current behaving as though the hot filament emitted negative electric particles. Today, we know that the emanations from the hot ball and the filament consist of electrons.

Some 20 years later, in 1906, Lee De Forest demonstrated that this current-in-vacuum is capable of extraordinarily sensitive control through the interposition, between the filament and the plate, of a gridlike structure that is almost transparent to electrons. Thus, he created the three-element electron tube, which ushered in our radio age (Figure 3).

In an electron tube, a cathode (hot metal) and an anode (positively charged plate) are enclosed in a vacuum (to remove oxygen which would burn up the metal and to remove air molecules which impede electron motion). With a battery's negative terminal connected to the cathode and its positive terminal to the anode, electrons flow from the battery to the cathode and thence across the vacuum to the anode.

A voltage applied to the grid literally dominates the current flow; large changes in the electron flow result from tiny changes in the grid voltage. A vibrating (varying) electric voltage applied to the grid compels the electron flow (current) to increase and decrease in exact unison with the pattern of the impressed voltage. But the power of the corresponding

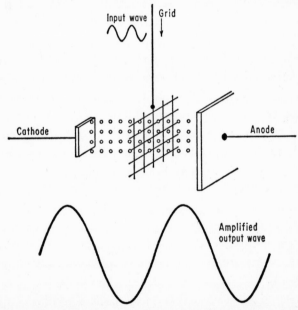

FIG. 3 The three-element electron tube (triode) amplifies a vibrating voltage applied to the grid by producing a more powerful replica in the electron stream.

variations in the current is much greater than that of the impressed voltage. Thus, the variations are amplified.

The amplification phenomenon may be applied in two ways. If the vibrations (which may be those of a voice) are fed into the input of a device and picked up at the output for conduction away to other circuits, then the device functions as an amplifier. Or, if the output is simply fed back into the input, a vibration (started perhaps by a random voltage change in the grid) goes round and round, and the device operates as an *oscillator,* a vibration generator, the dominant frequency of which can be rigidly controlled through suitable circuitry. By providing an effective, flexible, and economical device for generating and amplifying electromagnetic vibrations at what are now known as *radio frequencies,* the electron tube became the principal factor in making possible radio broadcasting and long-distance telephony.

A constant goal of technology has been to increase the operating frequency from the relatively low radio frequencies at which electron-tube communications began. The principle underlying this goal is that higher-frequency vibrations can carry more simultaneous information. Higher frequencies call for oscillators and amplifiers able to handle them. This brings us to the fact that every kind of oscillator, no matter what its physical form or principle, has some natural factor which limits the frequencies at which it can operate. The three-element electron tube has been successfully developed to oscillate at frequencies up to the microwave region. Here, it runs into an insurmountable barrier arising for the curious reason that the electrons are too slow in their reactions.

In a three-element tube oscillator, the electrons must move fast enough to travel from the cathode to the grid in much less time that it takes to execute a half cycle of the waves. Now, we think of electrons as being fast. Yet, at microwave frequencies the voltage alterations are too fast for the electrons to keep pace with, even though the distance from the cathode to the grid is purposely made as small as practicable.

For many years this limitation hampered the development of communications at microwave frequencies. Then, in 1938, there appeared upon the scene a new type of oscillator which its inventors named the *klystron* (after the Greek word *klyzein* that connotes the breaking of waves on the beach). In the klystron (Figure 4) the action occurs in a tuned cavity where radio waves are caused to resonate like sound waves in an organ pipe. At the same time, an energetic stream of electrons is propelled through the cavity. Reacting to the waves, the electron stream bunches up and thins out in unison with the crests and troughs of the waves. Thus, the waves draw energy from the electron stream and are amplified.

A decade later came another new device, named the *traveling-wave tube*. In this tube waves are made to race along with a stream of electrons from which the waves draw energy somewhat as ocean waves draw energy from a strong wind (Figure 5). The klystron and the traveling-wave tube lifted practical operating frequencies of communications well up into the microwave region. Here, the klystron, too, runs into its own peculiar natural limitation—the dimensions of its resonant cavity. Just as the dimensions of a resonant organ pipe decrease as we increase the pitch, so the dimensions of a klystron's resonant cavity decrease with rising frequency. At wavelengths of the order of a few millimeters the required dimensions become, for practical purposes, unattainable.

In addition to having their operating frequencies determined by tuned circuits or resonant cavities, all the wave generators we have mentioned share a single

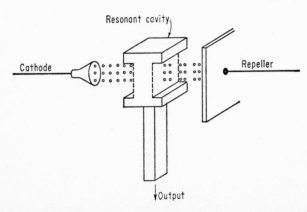

FIG. 4 The klystron tube causes amplifying interaction between the electron stream and waves in a resonant cavity.

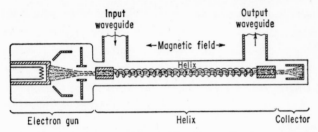

FIG. 5 A traveling-wave tube amplifies by causing interaction between waves traveling around a spiral conductor and an electron stream projected along the spiral's axis.

fundamental characteristic—all employ free electrons. And so it has been throughout the development of the application of radio oscillations to date. Beginning with the Leyden jar discharge, through Hertz's experiments, through the beginnings of long-distance voice radio in World War I, through the development of modern radio and TV broadcasting, microwave communications and satellites, the oscillations have been created in only one way—with pulsating masses of free electrons. This fact applies even to oscillators made with transistors, whose properties depend on the behavior of free electric charges, albeit in semiconductors.

In contrast, most of nature's electromagnetic waves are generated by the imperceptible motions of minute electric charges in individual atoms, positively or negatively charged atoms, molecules, and atomic nuclei. Let us next see how the study of natural radiation led to the concept and invention of the laser.

3 | ELECTROMAGNETIC RADIATION AND SPECTROSCOPY

Electromagnetic radiation tells us, through spectroscopy, about the inside of matter · How the science of spectroscopy began and developed · In conjunction with atomic theory it led to masers and lasers

Broadly speaking, we are interested in electromagnetic radiation for three reasons. We are interested in making sources of illumination and radiant heat that are ever more effective and convenient. We are interested in applying electromagnetic radiation to realize long-distance wireless communication. We are interested scientifically for what such radiation can tell us about the universe.

It goes without saying that light acquaints us with our immediate world; reflecting, refracting, scattering, absorbing, and emitting, it informs us about the surface and texture of our surroundings. Through astronomy, light along with other radiation informs us about the distant universe.

Less widely realized is the fact that electromagnetic radiation brings us information about the inner structure of matter which could not be obtained in any other way. Just as radio waves tell an experienced radio engineer, through their wavelength, pattern, and intensity, the kinds of oscillators, amplifiers, and antennas which probably make up an unidentified radio transmitter, so the radiation from matter tells us about the composition of atoms and molecules. To receive, record, and interpret the telltale signals sent to us by atoms and molecules is the task of the science of spectroscopy, which plays a major role in maser and laser physics.

Spectroscopy began three centuries ago when Sir Isaac Newton sent sunlight from a hole in a shutter through a glass prism to produce a band of colors which he named the *spectrum*. This classical experiment scientifically demonstrated that sunlight is complex, consisting of the seven basic colors, a fact which Mother Nature also beautifully demonstrates when she uses raindrops like prisms to produce rainbows. With Newton wrongly believing that light consists of material particles, there was at the time no adequate theory to explain the prism's action; and with no clues as to how the phenomenon might be applied, Newton's experiment lay dormant for well over a hundred years.

Early in the nineteenth century, interest revived with the discovery that Newton's visible spectrum spills over at both ends into invisible regions beyond. This happened when the astronomer W. Herschel discovered heat-generating infrared radiation extending beyond the red end of the spectrum and J. W.

Ritter detected the existence of invisible ultraviolet beyond the violet end.

How many other invisible regions might there be? This question and other developments, along with new speculations about the nature of light, whetted the appetite of early nineteenth-century physicists for further exploration. In 1802, Thomas Young, substituting his wave theory of light for Newton's corpuscular theory, calculated the approximate wavelengths of the seven colors, and spectroscopy became a rigorous science.

A prism reveals the composition of light by refracting (deflecting) each wavelength through a different angle. With a narrow slit of light as a source and optical devices to focus the incoming and outgoing beams of light, the spectrum appears as a sequence of colored rectangular images. Because an incandescent solid such as a lamp filament emits almost every frequency of light, the sequence merges into a continuous band of changing colors. If the light from an incandescent solid is sent through a substance which absorbs certain wavelengths, their positions in the spectrum are marked by dark lines. Then, too, since flames, electrical discharges, sparks, or gases and vapors emit only at specific wavelengths, their spectra consist of bright lines separated by intervals of darkness. Each type of atom and molecule emits or absorbs a uniquely characteristic spectrum—its own distinctive "signature" in electromagnetic radiation—which it is the task of the spectroscopist to determine.

Spectroscopy grows with its instrumentation. Over the years it has grown with prisms of better or different materials, the use of other devices such as diffraction gratings for separating the wavelengths, and the substitution of photographic film for the eye. The application of the diffractive action of atoms in crystals opened up the X-ray spectrum. More recently other techniques have broken through to the microwave (ultrahigh radio-frequency) region. Altogether spectroscopists have accumulated data on several million lines emitted or absorbed by atoms and molecules, data which constitute a gigantic dictionary of the electromagnetic language of matter and encompass 30 octaves in frequency range.

Probably no science is less known to the man on the street than that of spectroscopy. This is because it is a science which can never compete for the headlines with, for example, the dramatically visible and ostensibly comprehensible achievements of satellite science. Yet, probably no science contributes more to our information about the cosmos. Looking deeply into atoms in stars millions of light-years away, the perceptive eye of spectroscopy tells us the universe is composed of much the same stuff as our own earth. Detecting the minuscule shifts of spectral lines from their normal positions, it reveals that stars are spinning; and confirms the weird and disturbing hypothesis that the universe is constantly expanding. In partnership with theoreticians, spectroscopists have brilliantly helped to forge modern atomic theory. Among its recent achievements, spectroscopy paved the way to the invention of the maser, and today it continues to guide the search for new and more effective maser and laser mechanisms as well as more versatile and efficient materials.

How do atoms and molecules absorb and emit the radiation which the spectroscopist studies? Broadly, the answer is that the atom is a superbly versatile "machine" for absorbing, storing, and emitting radiation. To understand why, let us first consider how an atom is constructed and then examine some of the laws by which its activity is governed.

4 | THE ATOM AND
ITS ELECTRON WORLD

The nature of the atom · The atom's whirling array of planetary electrons · The energy that these electrons possess and how it may be changed · An energy analogy between electrons and bowling pins

We speak casually of the atom as if we know what it is. We don't. At any rate we do not know what an atom is in the sense that we know what a chair is, for a chair is something we can see and touch, whereas no one has ever seen or touched an individual atom.

Challenging us to entertain strange ideas which quarrel with our common sense, perhaps no product of the mind of man is more puzzling and paradoxical to most of us than the atomic theory of matter. Contrarily, when the theory is put to the test in our practical world, we find that no other piece of abstract reasoning about the universe more strikingly demonstrates its validity. (We need only mention that utterly convincing product, the atom bomb.) We are led to the conclusion that its strange concepts probably bring us closer to the inner truth of the physical universe than anything else in our seemingly real, comfortingly reassuring immediate world of chairs, children, and cheddar cheese.

For an understanding of masers and lasers, much about the world of the atom need not concern us at all. We need not, for instance, concern ourselves with that mysterious innermost realm of atomic nuclei, which, in addition to supplying more than 99.9 per cent of the world's weight, also supplies the enormous energy of atom bombs and atomic piles. We are here concerned only with the atom's outer world, the constellation of planetlike electrons which endlessly orbits the nucleus.

This restless array of electric charges wears one of many aspects, depending on the demands of its environment. Thus, in a gas, these satellite electrons exert powerful repulsive forces which at close quarters behave like spring buffers, causing atoms (or molecules, consisting of two or more atoms) to bounce off each other like billiard balls. Yet, when the same atoms or molecules approach each other under conditions that favor chemical bonding, the outermost electrons organize so as to fasten them together into rigid solids.

In some atoms the planetary electrons readily unite with those of all sorts of other atoms as, for example, in iron, which quickly rusts (combines with oxygen) when unprotected. In the so-called *inert* or *noble* gases such as neon, they unite with other atoms only under great compulsion. In still other situations (as we saw), some of these electrons leave their atoms to run electric motors, carry telephone messages, and launch radio waves; or again without ever leaving their atoms (as we shall see), they emit and absorb radiation, light neon signs, and operate masers.

Consider the simplest of all atoms, hydrogen (Figure 6). It consists of a nucleus of positive electricity (the proton), the space around which is ceaselessly "patrolled" by a solitary electron. Moving at nearly the speed of light, this electron does a lot of traveling for its size; if it were the size of a baseball, then proportionally a mile-wide sphere would be needed to encompass its flight. In its journey around the nucleus this electron is like the earth going around the sun; for just as the earth is held in by the sun's gravitational pull, so the negative electron is kept in captivity by the electric pull of the positive nucleus. And again, just as the earth's motion prevents the earth from being dragged into the sun, so the electron's motion prevents the electron from being dragged into the nucleus. Yet here the likeness ends, for while the earth pursues a simple, steady predictable orbit, the electron's motion in the atom cannot be observed. Theory— the so-called *uncertainty*

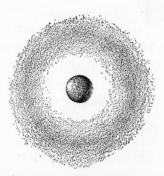

FIG. 6   The hydrogen atom's single electron produces a cloud of negative electric charge around the positive nucleus (which is shown disproportionately large).

principle—tells us that it is impossible to know precisely both the position and momentum of a particular electron at a particular instant. Even if we could catch the electron in a particular position, we could never determine whence it has come or whither it is headed. It is therefore quite impossible to follow a particular electron by plotting its path from instant to instant on graph paper as it is possible to plot the path of a curving baseball or a bullet in flight.

If an electron were a spot of light and your vision could follow its motion, you might see it move round and round, sometimes closer to the nucleus, sometimes farther away, to and fro, up and down, sometimes toward you, sometimes away, now and again doubling back on itself. In the next instant of this bewildering capriciousness, you would see it follow a totally different path—one of an infinitude of different paths, none of which could ever be predicted. Yet, if you continued to watch this motion for any length of time, you would see it form a regular pattern of varying density. That's because in its comings and goings the electron spends more time at one radius than another. The region of maximum density tells where the electron is spending most of its time.

Suppose that you could stand upon the nucleus of an atom and be ghostly enough for electrons to pass through you. You would then find yourself enveloped by a swirling "mist" of negative electricity. If, now, you walked away radially from the nucleus, it would be like walking through the vaporous wall of a phantom tennis ball, as the "mist" increased and decreased in density.

In odd contrast to its capricious motion, an orbiting electron possesses an amount of energy, the value of which is strictly fixed by the laws governing the atom and can be exactly calculated. Atomic science tells us that the amount of energy an orbiting electron may possess is determined by the domain or *shell* in which it is constrained to move. Also, there are many different shells corresponding to many different energies. In all atoms, the shell closest to the nucleus is known as the K shell. Hydrogen's single electron circulates in the K shell. However, the K shell can accommodate two electrons; the helium atom, having two electrons, therefore has a completely filled K shell.

Farther out from the nucleus we come upon the L shell, which houses as many as eight electrons. Even farther away are the still higher energy M and N shells, accommodating up to 18 and 32 electrons, respectively. Thus, in an atom with fully occupied K, L, M, and N shells, there can be as many as 60 orbiting electrons. Uranium, which has the most shells and electrons of all natural atoms, contains a total of 92 planetary electrons.

The shells are spherical, physicists tell us, unless they are interfered with by external forces. The com-

bining of atoms into solids comes from action in the
outermost shells. While the electrons in the protected
interior continue to pursue their rounded flight, the
outermost electrons may have to engage in complicated gyrations to adapt to the forces acting on them.
Instead of swinging around in a sphere, the electrons
may be squeezed into an oval or forced into some
even more intricate path. As we shall see, the electrons responsible for maser action in a ruby whirl
about in a course shaped like clover leaf.

The energy of orbiting electrons comes in several
different forms, and this is of crucial importance to
masers. To picture these various forms of energy let
us consider the kinds of energy which may be possessed by a conventional bowling pin. Think first of
a bowling pin resting on a shelf. Motionless, it nevertheless possesses energy—potential energy caused by
the pull of gravity. Knocked off the shelf and falling
to the ground, the pin develops *kinetic* energy, that
is, *motion* energy.

Broadly speaking, a body has potential energy when
a force is trying to push, pull, twist, or squeeze it. In
this instance, the force is one that pulls—the force
of gravity pulling on the body's mass. Also, the kinetic
energy that the pin develops in falling is due to motion of a particular kind—motion in a straight line.
But a body can also possess potential energy from
being acted on by other kinds of forces, and it can
have kinetic energy from other kinds of motion.

For instance, suppose that we have a second pin standing side by side with the first one. Suppose, too, that the pins are of metal and that they are charged with the same kind of electricity (positive or negative). Since like charges repel like charges, each pin tries to push the other away as though there were a compressed spring between them. (With electric charges of opposite sign, the pins would be attracted. The "spring" between them would be extended and so be under tension.) Thus, the electric forces endow the pins with still another source of energy, which results neither from the action of gravity nor from motion.

Suppose further, that each pin, in addition to being electrically charged, is also a magnet with a north pole at the top and a south pole at the bottom. Again, since like repels like, the two north poles repel each other as do the two south poles. There will be a force thrusting the pins apart. (If we turn one of them upside down, then the pins will be attracted.) Either way, the magnetic forces provide the pins with yet another source of potential energy.

Now assume, in addition, that each pin is a spinning top and that one of the tops is made to precess around its axis. Interacting electrically and magnetically one top affects the other, and presently the second top begins to precess in unison. Thus, the pins possess spin energy in addition to all other kinds of energy. Finally, we note that the pins are also in a state of vibration and therefore possess vibrational energy.

This complicated situation is governed by a great simplifying fact—each force and its associated energy leads a completely independent existence. Each force acts on the body, and each type of energy does its part as though the others do not exist. For example, the electric and magnetic action between the tops operate as though the gravitational pull on them were not there. If we could somehow convert the shelf into a catapult so as to hurl the pins into space, they would continue to interact electrically and magnetically as before, simply adding the kinetic energy of their motion through space.

In the variety of energies they possess, orbiting electrons are much like our imaginary bowling pins. Consider the single electron in a hydrogen atom. In its motion around the nucleus, this electron possesses kinetic energy due to the fact that it is a mass in orbital motion, and it has potential energy deriving from the attractive force exerted by the nucleus. Furthermore, since it is an electric charge with a spin motion, the electron behaves like a magnet, creating a magnetic field, interacting magnetically with other electrons and with the nucleus, which (being a spinning electric charge) is also a magnet.

As we add more electrons in more orbits, the possible energies become vastly more complicated; the electrons interact not only with the nucleus but also with each other, both electrically and magnetically, as they pursue their headlong journeys around the nucleus. Thus, we see that the atom's system of orbiting electrons constitutes a "machine" of versatile capabilities for storing energy.

The maser and laser became possible when we learned to manipulate this energy-storing "machine" in a particular way. How can we manipulate the energy of orbiting electrons? We noted that the energy of an orbiting electron is restricted to one or another fixed value. It can be in one orbit or another; it can also change energy while remaining in the same orbit, for example, by flipping over and pointing in the opposite direction magnetically. However, it can never possess an amount of energy intermediate between any two values prescribed by atomic law. Consequently, an electron in an atom can change its energy only by acquiring or losing a package of energy of one of several prescribed sizes.

Question: What kind of energy? *Answer:* The same that we use in telephony—electromagnetic energy—and this brings us face-to-face with still another dizzying concept of the atom world: the unit of electromagnetic energy called the *photon.*

5 | PHOTONS— PACKAGES OF ENERGY

The concept of the photon as the basic package of electromagnetic energy · In the atom world electromagnetic waves appear as streams of photons · Photons provide the key to changing and manipulating an atom's orbital electron energy

Ordinarily we picture radio waves as curving lines of crests and troughs cutting gracefully through space or time—the higher the crests and the deeper the troughs, the stronger the waves. In the world of the atom, a train of electromagnetic waves appears as a stream of energy packages called *photons*. Each photon has an amount of energy that is equal to a constant multiplied by the frequency of the waves. According to this view, if you generate a stream of photons all of the same energy, you generate a train of waves at a frequency corresponding to the photon energy. To amplify waves, you increase the concentration of the photons by adding more photons of the same energy or frequency.

How can radiation be at one and the same time a vibration—a wavy curve in space or time—and a stream of particle-like energy packages? This is a puzzling idea. Yet the evidence is overwhelming that radiation does indeed have two faces. This doesn't bother the physicist because he thinks of the situation mathematically and doesn't need to visualize. He has a photon hat and a wave hat, and carelessly he flips from one to the other, depending on whether it is expedient to take an atom scientist's point of view or that of a radio engineer.

The infinitesimal photon provides the key for changing and controlling an atom's orbital energy. When a photon of radiation impinging on an atom fits the difference between two of an atom's allowable energy levels, it actuates a specific orbital mechanism, racking up the energy from a lower to a higher level in what is called *absorption*. Conversely, the *emission* of a photon causes a reverse action in the mechanism and an energy decrease from a higher level to a lower level.

Consider, for example, the hydrogen atom. When a hydrogen atom absorbs a photon at a frequency of 1.4×10^9 cps (corresponding to a wavelength of 21 centimeters), its solitary electron turns a somersault so as to point in reverse direction magnetically. Conversely, in flipping back to its original position, it emits a characteristic 21-centimeter-wavelength photon (enabling us, incidentally, to identify the distribution of clouds of hydrogen in space). Absorption of a photon of much greater energy and at the much higher frequency of 10^{18} cps would jerk the electron out of the K shell up into the L shell. Thus, it is theoretically possible to excite the electron to higher and higher allowable energy levels, step by step, until the nucleus can no longer hold it in captivity, and it breaks away to exist as a free electron.

By recording, measuring, and analyzing the radiation given off by substances when they are excited by heat, electrical discharge, and electromagnetic radiation, spectroscopists and atomic scientists try to deduce the mechanisms responsible for the various lines. One line in particular acquired historical significance early in this century. This line, which has a wavelength of 1.25×10^{-5} centimeter and a frequency of 2.4×10^{15} cps, was known to be produced by excited hydrogen. It had been observed that, in the spectrum of hydrogen emitted by the sun, this line is missing; originating in excited hydrogen in the sun's interior, the energy is absorbed by unexcited hydrogen in the sun's exterior. Through what mechanism does the hydrogen atom both emit and absorb this line? From beginnings such as this, Niels Bohr constructed today's model of the atom.

At present, we feel that we have a sound understanding of the atomic mechanisms which are responsible for the spectral lines of many elements and compounds. In general each shell plays specific roles. For example, the K and L shells yield X rays, which are generated when a high-speed electron collides with a metallic atom. The impinging electron knocks out one of the two electrons in the K shell, adjacent to the nucleus. To fill the vacancy and restore the balance, an electron is pulled in from the L shell. The released energy emerges as a photon of X rays. Optical frequencies arise in the outer shells. Infrared may originate in interatomic vibrations within molecules, and microwaves in the rotation of entire molecules.

Every type of atom or molecule is marked by its own uniquely characteristic way of absorbing and emitting radiant energy. We noted some of the energy packages that might react with hydrogen. We saw how the energy could be raised step by step until the electron was torn away. Conversely, you might start with maximum energy and decrease it step by step.

Atoms and molecules form energy "ladders," each type of atom or molecule having its distinctive number of available rungs and distances between rungs. It was by learning how to manipulate such ladders that physicists succeeded in producing maser action. Long before that, we had learned to use them in neon signs and fluorescent lamps. For uncounted ages before, nature was using energy ladders to produce colors; let us next see how they operate to produce the warm red of rubies and the cold blue of sapphires.

6 | ATOMIC-ENERGY LADDERS

Atoms have energy "ladders" · How nature uses the chromium atom's ladder to make rubies red · How we use atomic ladders in neon and fluorescent lamps · How atoms in groups share energy · Absorption and emission · The concept of stimulated emission · Why substances ordinarily do not amplify · The concept of population inversion

In our appreciation of ruby and sapphire gems we perhaps think of them as completely different. Actually, they are very much alike in that both consist almost entirely of pure corundum—aluminum oxide. This material is transparent and colorless, which means that it freely transmits all the seven component colors of white light. The corundum of ruby and sapphire gems is mixed with very small amounts of impurities that absorb certain colors and let others through.

In the ruby gem a very few aluminum atoms—about 1 in every 5,000—are replaced by chromium atoms. It is these very few atoms which cause the ruby's color. In fact so far as color is concerned, the beautifully shaped crystal we hold in our fingers is simply a framework of aluminum and oxygen atoms which serves to hold the chromium atoms in place and provide them with an environment in which they can perform their distinctive color-control function.

As a result of the way the chromium atom is built and the forces which act upon it as part of the crystal, the chromium atom acquires spaces in its energy ladder which match violet and green photons. When white light enters, bringing in photons of the seven colors of the rainbow, the chromium atoms absorb the violet and green photons. At the same time they let through red and blue photons to produce the ruby's distinctive color. In a sapphire gem, the chromium is replaced by titanium, which absorbs red and green to produce sapphire blue.

Sometimes the ladder functions as a *frequency converter,* for it takes in radiation at one frequency and gives back radiation at another. This happens in the phenomenon known as *fluorescence*. In total darkness a ruby glows red when bathed in invisible ultraviolet. This occurs when the chromium atoms, having absorbed high-frequency ultraviolet, descend the ladder to emit, at a particular rung, lower-frequency red.

In a neon sign, the atoms of neon gas are subjected to bombardment by electrons energetic enough to rip other electrons from the outer orbits of the atoms. Lacking an electron and hence bearing a positive charge, the unbalanced atom soon attracts back a wandering electron. After shooting into high position on the ladder, the atom proceeds to descend. In the first stage of descent, energy is emitted at the high frequency of ultraviolet, which is invisible. Subsequently, as the atom's energy passes between another pair of rungs, it emits the characteristic pink of neon signs.

Sometimes invisible radiation from an atom of one kind is employed to excite visible radiation from atoms of another kind. This is done in the fluorescent lamp. An electric discharge in mercury vapor hoists the mercury atoms up their ladder. Descending, the atoms emit ultraviolet, which in turn strikes a special coating on the glass tube of the lamp and causes it to glow with characteristic luminosity.

Before leaving the ladder, let us consider for a moment its enormous range. From the topmost point where electrons are torn from the outermost orbits, down through the ultraviolet and green, down through the yellow and red to the infrared, finally we get to microwave radiation. Since the energy of a photon is proportional to its frequency, and since the frequency of microwaves (say, 10^9 cps) is only one hundred-thousandth that of light (say, 10^{14} cps), a microwave photon has only one hundred-thousandth the energy of a light photon. Hence, if we choose the distance of 1 foot between the rungs of our ladder to represent the energy difference for microwave frequencies, we would have to make the ladder over 20 miles long in order to encompass ultraviolet. In the laser, as we shall see, we work over the 20-mile range of the ladder, and in the maser over only 1 foot.

With some notable exceptions (one of which we shall come on in the helium-neon laser), atoms that have been hoisted up their energy ladders almost immediately come down again to the bottom-most rung, known as the atom's *ground state* and corresponding to the lowest energy state. Most atoms obey nature's tendency to keep systems at their lowest energy level and exist in the ground state unless they are jogged out of it by incoming photons or collisions with other atoms. Of great interest to maser and laser physics is what happens to the orbital energies of atoms and molecules that are found together in a material.

So far, we have spoken of atoms as though each existed as an isolated individual. We have done so in order to bring the atom and its energy-handling orbital mechanism into focus as clearly and simply as possible. Obviously, however, this is fictitious. Actually, atoms exist in company and interact with uncounted billions of others in gases, vapors, liquids, solids, and plasmas. Of particular interest to us here is how radiation interacts not with individual atoms but with populations of atoms and molecules, for it was by learning to manipulate this interaction in special ways that maser and laser actions were obtained.

Before examining the nature of such manipulations, let us review briefly some major advances through which our modern understanding of atoms and their interaction with radiation evolved. This modern understanding may be said to have begun around the year 1900, when the science of physics wrestled with the dilemma that a blackbody radiator, such as the sun, did not radiate in accordance with existing theory. While theory required that the radiation intensity must continually increase with rising frequency, measurements (Figure 22) showed that the intensity actually climbs to a maximum, then arches over and decreases as the frequency is carried still higher.

Most of us know how, in one of the most prognostic episodes in the history of science, the German physicist Max Planck discovered that he could explain this arching over of the blackbody radiation curve by assuming that the energy is emitted discontinuously, in packages or *quanta,* each having an energy equal to some constant multiplied by the frequency of vibration. Opening the way to our present-day sophisticated and competent quantum mechanical theory of matter, this simple idea turned out to be one of the great revolutionary concepts of physical science.

Soon thereafter, in 1905, Albert Einstein showed how the quantum view not only explained blackbody radiation but could also exactly and convincingly explain the photoelectric effect in which a metal exposed to light emits electrons. Less than 10 years later came the celebrated application of the quantum idea to the orbital electron system of atoms.

Although the concept of the atom itself is of ancient origin, having been expounded by the Greek philosopher Democritus 2,300 years ago, its application as a working entity of science is of comparatively recent origin. In the intervening years the idea must have been toyed with by many a mind probing the mysteries of matter, but it languished for want of an effective theory in which to become embodied.

In the first part of the nineteenth century, the English chemist John Dalton developed a scientific theory that saw all atoms of any one element as exactly alike and the atoms of different elements as combining into molecules to form compounds. In the second half of the nineteenth century came the gradual realization that the atom is not, after all, an entity, one and indivisible, but actually consists of smaller particles. Particularly, it must involve—it came to be seen—electrons.

The existence of a particle much smaller than the smallest atom was first revealed by the study of the cathode rays produced when an electric discharge is passed through an evacuated tube. Extensive study of the cathode ray and associated phenomena went on to establish the existence of a negatively charged particle having a mass $1/1,837$ that of the hydrogen atom. Adopting a word that had been coined by D. Johnston Stoney back in 1881, the scientists named the particle *electron*.

With evidence piling up that electrons must be constituents of atoms, it became necessary to postulate that the electrically neutral chemical atom must also possess a counterbalancing positive charge. In 1911, Sir Ernest Rutherford announced the so-called *nuclear model* of the atom in which the atom is seen to consist of a positive charge concentrated in a heavy central nucleus of very small dimensions and surrounded by a cluster of negative electrons. In terms of the existing theory, this model rationally explained the existence of the atom as a system of counterbalanced electric charges, but also it presented two prime difficulties: the theory could not delineate an electron's orbit around the nucleus, and it could not explain why radiating electrons do not eventually collapse into the nucleus as a result of loss of energy.

Attacking the problem, the Danish physicist Niels Bohr showed that the energy-package concept that had enabled Planck to explain blackbody radiation and Einstein to account for the photoelectric effect could also explain what went on in the nuclear model of the atom. In 1913, Bohr showed that electrons conform to a strict law which permits them to move around only in such ways that conform to certain precisely definable energy states.

How the Bohr atom and its illustrious partner, the quantum theory, joined forces and evolved into our present sophisticated understanding of the atom world has been covered over and over again in the literature of science. Significantly, these accounts contain little or no mention of another finding that also came out of this classical ferment of ideas although it embodied, we see in retrospect, primary clues to maser and laser action. This came about in 1917 when

Einstein, following his predilection for synthesizing approaches, worked out in a detailed manner the behavior of matter when it exists in equilibrium with radiation.

Consider a population consisting of atoms of a gas and of photons shut up together in a box with perfectly reflecting walls. Under the energy of heat the atoms are in violent motion, bouncing like golf balls off each other and off the walls of the box. Through various processes the atoms acquire, emit, and generally exchange energy. For instance, between atoms and energetic free electrons, there are collisions in which an atom may be excited to a higher level and subsequently return to ground level by emitting a photon. The latter, after bouncing off the walls, may eventually be reabsorbed by another atom. Thus, there is a continuing interchange of energy that always produces some atoms which are at a level above the ground state.

Drawing on the current thinking and adding some of his own, Einstein postulated that there are three ways in which an atom may interact with a photon. First, if an unexcited atom is struck by a photon having an energy equal to a space in the atom's energy ladder, the photon is probably *absorbed* into the atom's orbital system. Second, if nothing further happens to the atom, it will sooner or later *spontaneously* emit this stored energy. Third, if a photon strikes an excited atom—an atom that has a photon "in storage"—it will *stimulate* the atom to emit its stored photon—provided the energy of the stored photon is equal to that of the impinging photon.

Putting together the three phenomena—absorption, spontaneous emission, and stimulated emission —Einstein arrived through mathematical analysis at a rational picture of what happens when radiation exists in a state of equilibrium with matter. The result, however, was scarcely noticed outside a select group of mathematical physicists who were interested in the interaction of radiation with matter. It could not be suspected that one of these phenomena, namely stimulated emission, was destined to provide the basis for maser and laser action and would thus become one of the important physical concepts of our time.

Even when Einstein introduced the concept into his equations, the broad idea of stimulated emission was not new; it had, indeed, been contained in the theory of resonance and wave motion developed 40 years earlier by Lord Rayleigh. What Einstein did was to introduce it to quantum theory and bring it into focus as an indispensable part of the interaction between radiation and populations of atoms.

Let us see now how stimulated emission can be harnessed to amplify. We know that to amplify waves we must make them stronger without altering their frequency, and—as it appears in the atomic world—a wave train is a stream of photons of specific energy value depending on the frequency. Consequently, to amplify a wave train we must add to its representative stream of photons more photons of exactly the same energy.

Imagine, now, that we project a stream of photons through a material that possesses energy-level differences corresponding to the energy of the projected photons. If the projected photons strike unexcited atoms, they will be absorbed so that photons are removed from the stream and the wave train loses energy. If, instead, the projected photons strike excited atoms, they will knock out more photons; hence we add photons, amplifying the waves. Thus, the projected photons are subjected to opposed activities, one of which produces attenuation while the other produces amplification. Amplification occurs when the stimulated emission overrides the absorption, and this, in turn, can occur only when there are more excited atoms than unexcited ones. Ordinarily it does not occur in materials in their natural state because of the way in which nature arranges the atomic population at various energy levels.

Suppose we have a bottle of atoms that may exist at three energy levels. Suppose also that we have somehow managed to obtain an equal number of atoms at each level. Now, let us leave the bottle alone and watch what happens. At once the atoms engage in the process of transferring energy from one to another and to their surroundings. If, after a while, we could again count the atoms at each level, we would find a minority of them at the topmost level, more at the intermediate level, and most of all at the lowest level. This tendency of atoms to crowd the lower levels applies equally whether the atoms are loosely congregated in a gas, or concentrated in a liquid, or rigidly anchored together in a solid.

The law that governs nature's energy distribution was worked out in the last century by Maxwell and Boltzmann years before the advent of the modern concept of the atom or of photons or quantum theory. It was worked out on the basis of thermodynamic principles for gases in which particles are shut up together and must share heat energy. It applies equally to atoms sharing radiant energy.

In Figure 7 we show this law (Boltzmann's distribution law) expressed as a mathematical curve. The sweep of this curve tells us how the population of a system of atoms—an apple, a safety pin, or a ruby— is permitted to divide up on an energy basis. We note that there are almost no atoms at the topmost level and enormously great numbers of them on the lowest levels, rather as in human society where the poorest are the most abundant. The electron system of atoms, the curve tells us, may have an almost infinite number of possible energy levels. In specific atoms and molecules, however, the number of levels available depends upon the number of electrons, orbits, and other factors that enter into the energy-storing mechanism.

Because substances in their natural condition always have fewer atoms at the higher levels than at the lower levels, they can never amplify. Conversely, amplification can be achieved only by upsetting the natural state of affairs, by building up an unnaturally large population at some higher levels. Physicists call this *inverting* the population. Actually the requisite upsetting of the thermodynamic equilibrium can be obtained without inversion, but the processes involved do not concern the devices described in this book.

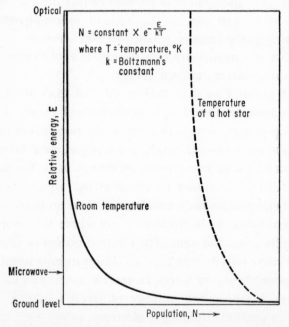

FIG. 7 Boltzmann's energy distribution curve prescribes the relative populations of particles or atoms that can exist at various energy levels in a material at a specific temperature.

Although the concepts of stimulated emission and population inversion were implicit in the theory of the interaction between matter and radiation, no one appreciated (at least nobody announced) that the phenomena might be applied to make an amplifier. Indeed, some 37 years were to elapse before they would come to be applied in the first maser. What were the forces that delayed the development? What were the forces that eventually brought it about? The answer is an interesting illustration of how new ideas gradually come into focus and, when the climate is right, become usefully applied.

7 | THE FIRST MASER

The first maser and the background in which it was created · Generic ideas and how they came into focus · Why the maser wasn't invented in the 1930s · The vital influence of a sophisticated micro-wave technology · The three keys to maser and laser action

Stimulated emission was observed as far back as 1924 but was not thought of as such. The occasion was a study of optical dispersion—the breaking up of light by materials into different frequencies. Theory had it that the dispersing medium consisted of minute resonators or oscillators. Under the impact of incident light, these oscillators were supposed to absorb energy, thus reducing the intensity of the light. In contrast, the results disclosed that, while some of the oscillators must be absorbing radiation as predicted, others were actually doing no such thing—they were emitting radiation.

Since these maverick oscillators appeared to be working in reverse from what was expected, the investigators dubbed them *negative oscillators* and went on to speak of *negative dispersion*. Today, we see the effect as a type of stimulated emission that could lead to population inversion. In the following years experimenters tried to increase the effect of negative dispersion but did not succeed to an extent that could produce marked inverted population. The effect was again observed in the 1930s, but again the clues were not actively pursued. There was no incentive; more important angles seemed to demand attention.

In judging what is worthwhile, we are inevitably influenced by the prevailing mental climate of our time. During those days when quantum mechanical theory was being developed, spectroscopists were primarily concerned with exploring and explaining the structure of atoms and molecules in terms of the new theory, either to confirm the theory or to discover and account for discrepancies. They had plenty to do. Stimulated emission was only one of numerous effects, and there was no dominating reason to study it. Then came World War II and with it powerful new combinations of forces of mental climate, knowledge, and instrumentation.

Perhaps we think of science as the leader in the discovery of new knowledge and of technology as waiting upon science, waiting to apply the new knowledge that science has uncovered. Sometimes the tables are turned, and scientific discovery must wait until technology has supplied the tools which are destined to make new insights possible. An illustration is the discovery of maser action, the discovery of which was greatly hastened by the existence at the end of the war of a sophisticated microwave technology.

Microwave technology—the art of handling waves

ranging from approximately 10^9 cps (30 centimeters) to 3×10^{10} cps (10 centimeters)—has turned out to be one of the giants of our time. By pushing electronic technology far up the frequency spectrum, microwave technology made effective radar possible in wartime. After the war, it enabled radio-beam highways of great traffic capacity; more recently it made satellite communication possible. To the science of physics microwave technology presented an instrumentation and a provocative viewpoint that would lead to the maser.

As to viewpoint, it is impressive how one discipline picks out and concentrates on those factors of the physical world that can best further its purposes while other disciplines may think of the same factors only as elements of theory. This applies to some extent to the phenomenon of resonance. Though basic to all nature, resonance was much less of a practical reality to physics than it was to communications, where it is an indispensable tool of the trade. It is, indeed, at the very heart of radio, for which the classical Leyden jar (a capacitor) with an associated inductor made possible the first transmission of radio waves while incoming waves are picked up by still another resonant circuit at the receiver. Then too, in a way, our electronic age began when the triode was first applied to activate resonant circuitry. Later, when the klystron came, it was fundamentally as another kind of resonator that it succeeded. The electric-wave filter, which separates waves by frequency in communications circuits, is, broadly speaking, a modified and sophisticated resonant circuit. Also, the resonant-circuit concept plays a major role in every part of the telephone highway, throughout the path of the voice right up to and including the telephone instrument.

Microwave researchers quickly discovered that wire circuits with their conventional capacitors, inductors, and resistors cannot effectively handle microwave vibrations, which they dissipate as heat or radiation.

To handle microwaves, first for radar and subsequently for communications generally, it became imperative to develop entirely new techniques in which waves were filtered and conducted by pipes called waveguides while they were generated and controlled by means of the resonant properties of cavities such as that of the klystron.

Among the good winds that blew in World War II was that which brought together physics and electrical engineering. Physicists and electrical engineers found themselves working side by side on problems that could not have been so readily solved by either group working alone. It is clearly not possible to predict the ultimate and total consequences of this fruitful interaction. Here, the point pertinent to our theme is the introduction of the physicist to the electronic arts, particularly to the working concept, approach, and technology for handling the microwave region of the spectrum. At one time, the electronics engineer and the physicist seemed to be poles apart as the former concerned himself with circuits and electronic hardware while the latter thought in terms of atoms, molecules, and their internal construction. In those days, many a physicist gazed with limited respect upon the electrical engineering art; for his part the engineer viewed with suspicion the empyrean flights of abstract reasoning through which the physicist so often seeks fundamentally new knowledge. Now the two disciplines have been forced together. Moving into the microwave region, the electrical engineer finds himself dealing with resonant cavities that must get ever smaller, eventually becoming unreasonably small as the frequency is carried ever higher. By the end of World War II, the shortest waves that could be generated by electronic means were about 6 millimeters long. Here the appropriate cavity borders on impracticability. To go very much higher in frequency, it would be necessary to go to molecular dimensions—in fact, to molecules. Thus, in the problem of handling such infinitesimal waves the disciplines of communications engineering and physics were brought together.

At the end of the war there were physicists who were not only familiar with microwave technology but were also interested in spectroscopy. They applied microwave technology to determine the spectra (and thus deduce the atomic and molecular mechanisms) of materials that react strongly in the microwave region.

In 1946, the application of microwave technology to explore the vigorous resonance phenomena exhibited in certain crystals brought out evidence for population inversion. In 1951, there occurred further experiments at radio frequencies with lithium fluoride; marked stimulated emission was not only obtained but was also clearly recognized.

Gradually, the phenomenon of stimulated emission, which had been only a factor in Einstein's radiation equations and which in the 1920s and 1930s had been observed to occur but did not seem to merit substantial study, now took on an intriguing and challenging reality. In the few years prior to the advent of the maser, the idea of applying stimulated emission to produce usable amplification entered into the speculations of several physicists both here and abroad. It could be seen from Einstein's radiation theory and the accumulating evidence for both stimulated emission and population inversion that such an amplifier must be possible. The specific problem—a truly formidable one—was to devise an effective technique. Why was it that the first technique to be arrived at employed ammonia and operated at microwave frequencies?

At the time, oscillators of the electronic type had succeeded in encompassing the frequency range all the way from waves many miles in length, such as are used in marine radar, down to waves a few millimeters long. Hot bodies such as the sun, incandescent filaments, arc lights, and gas discharges, using the oscillations of atoms and molecules, produced strong radiation at optical frequencies. Intriguingly, no one knew of an atomic or molecular mechanism capable of producing strong radiation in the so-called *submillimeter* range (wavelengths between 0.1 and 1.0 millimeter). This "no-man's land" of radiation challenged the imagination of radiation physicists generally; with notable consequences it challenged the inventor of the maser. Where might the answer lie?

The science of spectroscopy pointed the way. As we noted earlier, in their efforts to relate spectral lines with the structure of atoms and molecules, spectroscopists try to work with atoms and molecules that are simple enough to visualize and calculate and that can be caused to strongly emit or absorb radiation. For this reason, the ammonia molecule (Figure 8), with its relatively simple structure consisting of one nitrogen atom and three hydrogen atoms arranged in a pyramid, had come in for considerable study and was very well understood. It exhibits strong spectral lines in the submillimeter range. Was there some physical means through which ammonia molecules could be harnessed to amplify at submillimeter wavelengths?

Here, a dominating factor entered: There was no

adequate technology for the manipulation of radiation at submillimeter frequencies. At the same time, ammonia also exhibited a strong spectral line at approximately 1.3 centimeters or 2.4×10^{10} cps—a wavelength that could be effectively handled by existing microwave technology. Thus, again, the compelling presence of a competent technology determined the direction of a scientific advance. It was decided to concentrate on making a device that would operate at the microwavelength of 1.3 centimeters.

How could the population be inverted to obtain more molecules at the higher (emitting) level than at

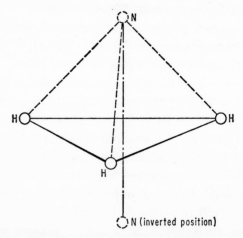

FIG. 8 The ammonia molecule consists of three atoms of hydrogen and one of nitrogen arranged in a pyramid. "Inversion" of nitrogen through a plane of hydrogen atoms causes an energy change equal to a photon of frequency of 2.387×10^{10} cps (1.26 centimeters wavelength). (*Adapted from "Masers," by J. R. Singer, John Wiley & Sons, Inc.*)

the lower level? The scientists took advantage of the already known fact that ammonia gas molecules react to a nonuniform electric field in ways that depend on their energy level. This offered a way to physically segregate the high-energy molecules. In the first of all masers ammonia gas is caused to flow through a specially designed cylinder; here an electric field draws the low-energy molecules away to the sides of the cylinder while the high-energy molecules flow through, into a cavity (Figure 9).

With a large excess of high-energy molecules the cavity is set for maser action. A 2.4×10^9 cps photon entering this energy-laden gas soon encounters a high-energy molecule and knocks out another 2.4×10^9

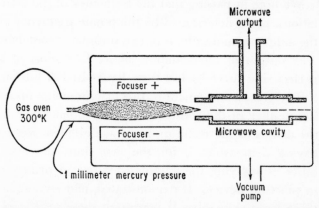

FIG. 9 The ammonia beam maser. Hot ammonia gas is propelled by pressure difference through a focuser, which extracts low-energy molecules. High-energy molecules continue into the tuned cavity to engage in amplification. (*Adapted from "Masers," by J. R. Singer, John Wiley & Sons, Inc.*)

cps photon, thus producing amplification. Unaided, however, the process is not intense enough to build up a vibration of usable strength.

It was crucial to the success of the device that its inventor understood that there would have to be a way to intensify the action and, furthermore, that intensification could be obtained by harnessing the phenomenon of resonance. He designed the cavity to resonate at 2.4×10^9 cps. In the reverberant space the photons are kept rocketing back and forth through the energy-loaded gas so as to build up a vigorous sustained oscillation. A 2.4×10^9 cps vibration entering the cavity is amplified 20 decibels (100 to 1 in power).

We note in passing that the frequency of the oscillations, being determined by the innate frequency of the ammonia molecule, is of extraordinary constancy. The output of the ammonia maser falls short of a perfect sine curve by less than 1 part in 100 billion.

The great achievement of this first ammonia maser lies neither in the constancy of its frequency nor in the details of the techniques; its achievement lies in having demonstrated, for the first time, the feasibility of applying the stimulated-radiation principle in practical devices. It demonstrated, and embodied, three basic principles. If you grasp these principles, you will then have a broad understanding of masers and lasers regardless of the materials or techniques they employ or the frequencies at which they operate. Let us summarize the three keys.

Key No. 1: Find a material which energetically emits at the frequency at which you want to work. (In the first maser the ammonia molecule strongly emits at 2.4×10^9 cps.)

Key No. 2: Find a way to invert the population so that the stimulated emission overrides absorption. (In the first maser this is done by physically segregating the lower energy molecules.)

Key No. 3: Intensify the action. (In the first maser this is done by staging the action in a resonant cavity.)

8 | TRAVELING-WAVE RUBY MASERS

The traveling-wave ruby maser · The incentive: to make a low-noise tunable maser amplifier · How paramagnetic crystals came to be used in masers · How certain orbital electron-magnets are harnessed · The application of a magnetic field for tuning · Some benefits derived from microwave technology

Once the maser principle had been definitely established by the ammonia gas maser as an applicable physical reality, interested physicists saw, from general theoretical considerations and the known characteristics of materials, that it must also be applicable with other materials and at other frequencies. What material? And at what frequencies? Should it or could it be made to operate with a gas, perhaps—a liquid, vapor, or solid? We speak grandly as though there were a wide choice. Actually there was not.

In the dazzling parade of scientific advances that marks our modern scene, we may be inclined to forget how little we actually know. For example, in the problem of what causes the behavior of materials we move in a vast ocean of ignorance, dotted here and there by tiny islands—points of inquiry at which, through patient and determined scientific effort, we have managed at last to acquire an effective understanding. It is by establishing such islands, then learning how to connect them, that we advance in knowledge. Within a short time, maser research headed for one of these islands—the subtle and fascinating world of the paramagnetic crystal. Among the incentives was the desire to make a maser amplifier that would be free of two important limitations inherent in the ammonia maser.

A maser, it was axiomatic, must be, by its very nature, almost free of the internal *noise* that plagues electronic amplifiers. As an amplifier, the maser therefore offered effective means for amplifying weak radio signals such as come in from the distant heavens through a radio telescope or to a ground receiver (yet to be built at the time) of a satellite system. Still, as an amplifier rather than as an oscillator, the ammonia maser has two severe limitations: Since its frequency is determined by the invariable frequency of the ammonia molecule, it is untunable; also, the band of frequencies it can handle is extremely narrow, far too narrow, for example, for satellite communication.

Another factor in directing maser development was the existence of a considerable understanding of paramagnetic crystals. Unlike most crystals, which are nonmagnetic, paramagnetic crystals contain atomic or molecular mechanisms that react to an applied magnetic field. The phenomenon had been considerably studied at microwave frequencies. From what was known, pioneer maser physicists theorized and then demonstrated practically that certain crystals could not only supply maser action but also a satisfyingly wide frequency band. Furthermore, such an amplifier could be tuned by adjusting the strength of the applied magnetic field.

In the earliest experiments more than one type of paramagnetic crystal was tried and found to produce maser action, but soon the major interest focused on the ruby, crystals of which can be readily grown in the desired size and purity. Here, we shall skip the early stages of the pioneer work and limit ourselves to a discussion of the action in the ruby. Particularly we shall describe the action in the traveling-wave ruby maser amplifier, which so brilliantly performed in the historic Echo and Telstar experiments.

The ability of a magnetic field to reach into a material and affect its radiating mechanisms was first observed in 1896. At that time what might be called magnetism in massive action, such as occurs in a hunk of iron magnetized by an electric current to form an electromagnet, was well known and had already been applied in such classical advances as the telegraph and telephone, the dynamo, and the electric motor. It was then that the Dutch physicist Pieter Zeeman made the important discovery that magnetism also operates in more subtle ways.

Placing a sodium flame between the poles of a powerful electromagnet, he discovered that the sodium's spectral lines were markedly broadened. Although then a sodium flame was thought of as non-magnetic, in some unexplained way the magnetic field reached into the flame and affected the radiating mechanisms. Thereafter, an applied magnetic field was found to affect spectra of other materials, and soon it became a powerful tool in the exploration of the structure of matter, helping to clarify and estab-lish modern atomic theory. It was to become a prin-cipal tool in harnessing the paramagnetic crystal to amplify microwaves.

To be affected by an applied magnetic field a sub-stance must contain mechanisms capable of reacting magnetically. Since all atoms involve spinning elec-trons, each of which is a magnet, it may be surpris-ing that all substances are not magnetic. Actually they are not magnetic because in most substances each electron-magnet has a compensating mate that spins in the opposite direction and is therefore oppositely magnetized. The net effect of these balanced pairs of electron-magnets is zero. The atoms of most sub-stances are magnetically neutral; we cannot affect them by applying a magnetic field; the substance as a whole is nonmagnetic. In contrast we have highly magnetic materials such as iron that involve huge numbers of magnetic elements interlocked to pro-duce magnetic effects. Between the two extremes is the relatively delicate and critically useful magnetism of the paramagnetic crystal. Let us see what atom science has to tell us about the action in a ruby.

We may well marvel at the sophisticated compe-
tence of modern atom science, a discipline barely 50
years old. It has long been customary to wonder at
the achievements of the ancient science of astronomy
in such matters as the exact calculation of the paths
of stars and planets and the seemingly uncanny prediction of eclipses and return of comets. Without
wishing to belittle these feats, we must point out that
the objects with which the astronomer deals have the
enormous advantage of being seeable. Peering into
the universe in the direction opposite from the astronomer, so to speak, the atomic physicist deals with
submicroscopic objects which have never been seen
and may indeed never be seeable at all. Nevertheless,
atom theory enables him to "go into" a material,
right into an atom, into the system of electrons that
wheels around the nucleus. There the physicist can
pinpoint the particular mechanism, even the particular submechanism, that causes the external phenomena we observe.

Atom science tells us that only a very small part
of a ruby performs the function of making it red and
that an even smaller portion engages in the magnetic
activity that permits maser action. Consisting essentially of pure sapphire, a ruby is composed almost
entirely of aluminum and oxygen atoms tightly
bonded to form a substance which is second in hard-
ness only to the diamond. The crystal is magnetically
neutral except for occasional spots—about 1 in 5,000

—where the position of an aluminum atom has been usurped by chromium. Here occurs the magnetic activity that is harnessed for maser action.

At each of these sites, a chromium atom is bonded to an atom of aluminum and another of oxygen. With each of the three nuclei attended by its family of electrons, we have a total array of some 45 electrons. These 45 electrons are magnetically compensated—all except three of them that move in the outer orbit of the chromium atom. Because of the way the chromium atom latches on to its neighboring aluminum and oxygen atoms, these three electrons do not have magnetically compensating mates. They are magnetically unbalanced; they behave like bar magnets. In the presence of a magnetic field, the three electrons possess an amount of energy that depends on the angle at which they point with respect to the field. This phenomenon provides one of the numerous mechanisms through which an atom's orbital-electron system can absorb and emit radiation.

The crystal has a natural magnetic field caused by its moving electric charges. Theory allows that the aggregate energy the three "magnets" can possess in the natural crystal may be at one of two levels. It is this aggregate energy that we manipulate by applying to the crystal a magnetic field, adding its effect to that of the internal field. The "magnets" behave as though locked together, moving from one orientation to another as a single bar magnet. According to the quantum theory, this "bar magnet" may point in one of four directions corresponding to four energy levels.

By ordinary standards an extraordinary achievement has been made. We have actually reached into the crystal and, by applying a magnetic field, split two energy levels into four. Moreover, the differences between these energy levels felicitously correspond to photons at microwave frequencies. We also see, from Figure 10, that by adjusting the strength of the field, we can control the levels to provide an appreciable range of energy-level differences, that is, microwave frequencies. Thus, by properly choosing the strength of the field, we can virtually "tune in" any particular energy-level difference.

To return to our earlier analogy, we have essentially constructed an atomic ladder that is operable by means of microwave photons. By injecting a photon of the appropriate energy or frequency, we can raise an atom from level 1 to level 2 or to levels 3 or 4. When the atom unloads this energy, it may give off an amount corresponding to the difference between levels 3 and 2 let us say. Since (as we see from Figure 10) the various level differences are markedly unequal, we can engage in pushing some atoms up the ladder while other atoms are emitting; because the frequencies involved are different, there will be no interference. Thus, we can conduct a sort of two-ring photon circus. This, in effect, is what is done in the traveling-wave ruby maser.

The maser amplifies at a frequency corresponding to the energy difference between levels 1 and 2. To bring this about, it is necessary to produce an unnaturally large population of chromium atoms in level 2. As the first step, the crystal is subjected to a stream of photons equal to the energy difference between levels 1 and 3; the effect of this is to hoist

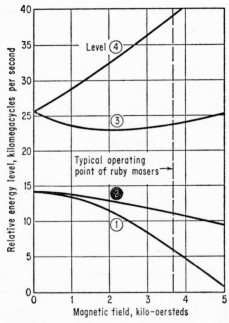

FIG. 10 Energy level versus applied magnetic field in the ruby. A typical traveling-wave tube maser operates at an energy difference between levels 1 and 2 corresponding to 4.2×10^9 cps (7.14 centimeters wavelength).

numerous atoms up from level 1 to level 3. Acting to dispose of this surplus, the crystal promptly extracts a portion of the energy and radiates it away as a photon (at a frequency which does not concern us here). As a result of the energy loss, the atom slips down to level 2. In this way we artificially supply a surplus of atoms to level 2. This is what we want, but one more condition must be fulfilled to obtain amplification. If the atoms drop out of level 2 as fast as newcomers arrive, we cannot establish a significant surplus.

The problem is like that of filling a bathtub with the drain open: The water must come in faster than it drains away; in effect the output must be delayed with respect to the input. Likewise, it is necessary to have a delay in the departure of atoms from level 2. Felicitously, the crystal itself supplies the necessary delay. There is a delay (we know from microwave spectroscopy) of $^{150}/_{1,000}$ second between the time of arrival of atoms in level 2 and the time of their departure—long enough for a surplus of atoms to pile up and become available for amplification.

The general physical arrangements for "pumping" the crystal are shown in Figure 11, which also shows most of the other important features of a microwave maser amplifier. The result of the pumping alone is weak, producing only a slight excess population in level 2—not nearly enough to sustain strong ampli-

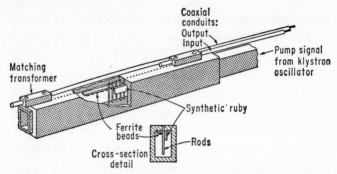

FIG. 11 The traveling-wave tube maser, simplified. The magnet and cooling chamber, which surround this structure, are not shown. Metal rods slow the signal to prolong the interaction with the ruby. Ferrite beads provide isolator action and prevent harmful signal reflections within cavity. "Pump" energy from a klystron oscillator, at approximately three times the frequency of the signal to be amplified, is absorbed by the crystal. Transformers match the impedance of coaxial leads to that of the cavity.

fication. The physicists got around this obstacle by again applying their knowledge of how atoms behave in large populations.

We saw that atoms interchange thermal and orbital energies and that the populations at various energy levels conform to the curve shown in Figure 7. As the temperature rises, the action becomes more violent, and more and more atoms are held at the higher levels: the curve straightens out, becoming theoretically vertical at infinite temperatures. Thus, in the interior of a hot star, we might find almost as many atoms at the higher levels as at the lower levels.

Maser physicists take advantage of the situation in reverse direction. Just as heat stimulates activity, so cold reduces it. The ruby is subjected to extreme cold, which pulls many more atoms down to level 1 and makes many more atoms available for the pump to raise up and deposit in level 3. The end result, as shown in the right-hand set of bars in Figure 12, is a larger surplus of atoms in level 2 and strong amplification. For maximum gain, the crystal is cooled to the lowest practically obtainable temperature by immersion in liquid helium.

And now we come to the third key—intensification of the action. In the ammonia maser the action was intensified by having the radiation shuttle to and fro in a resonant cavity. A resonant cavity is, by its very nature, sharply frequency-selective. To get a wide band another approach was in order.

The designers arranged for the incoming signal to

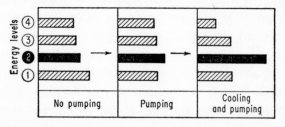

FIG. 12 Population changes in ruby maser action. The microwave signal gains photons from level 2, loses them to level 1. The "pump" signal raises atoms from level 1 to level 3. As atoms pour into level 3, they drop rapidly to level 2, and thereafter comparatively slowly to level 1. The result is a small surplus of atoms in level 2 (*center*) and some amplification of the signal. A cooled crystal provides more atoms in level 1 for the pump to raise to level 3. This leads to more atoms in level 2 (*right*), hence stronger amplification.

enter a cavity at one end, pass through an excited ruby, then emerge amplified at the other end—and with no reflections. To produce sufficient interaction between the ruby rod and the signal, the designers drew upon the traveling-wave-tube art. In the traveling-wave tube, waves are amplified by causing them to interact with an electron stream. Since waves travel much faster than electrons, it is necessary to slow down the waves to secure sufficient interaction. This is accomplished by making the waves travel round and round a spiral while the electron stream travels a much shorter distance along the spiral's axis. In our maser a row of metal rods lined up like fence posts along the length of the ruby act like a brake and slow down the photons, thus providing time for them to meet with, and stimulate, excited atoms.

For best amplifier performance, the signal energy must go right on through; none must be reflected. To prevent reflections, the designers drew upon another phase of the microwave art in which the direction of motion of waves is controlled through the magnetic action of ferrites. A row of tiny ferrite beads placed along the base of the rod fence converts the cavity into a "one-way street"; the signal travels through with almost no reflections.

We now come to the reason why the device is capable of amplifying over a broad band of frequencies. We saw that the frequency of the emitted radiation depends rigidly on the energy-level difference we stimulate. In the ammonia maser we utilize an energy-level difference that is inherent in the ammonia molecule and is therefore invariable. In the ruby maser, the energy level that we select by fixing the strength of the applied field at an appropriate value does not have a constant value; inevitably, as a result of the internal situation in the crystal, it varies over a band of frequencies. The reason for this is that the value of the magnetic field to which the three electrons are actually subject is not exactly equal to that of the field we apply; they are also subject to the magnetic forces exerted by neighboring atoms. The latter vary slightly from atom to atom, causing variations in the net magnetic field and, hence, in energy levels. As a result different atoms react to different incoming frequencies. This is of great benefit, for as a whole the crystal reacts to, and can thus amplify, frequencies varying over a range of 25×10^6 cps—a range theoretically sufficient to amplify simultaneously 7,000 voices or five TV programs.

Atoms in numbers beyond our imagining are called into play. In a typical 5-inch maser ruby there are 6×10^{22} atoms. Of these about 1 in 5,000 or 12×10^{18} are energy-storing chromium. The energy in each microwave photon is only 4×10^{-24} watt-second, but its impact on energy-laden level 2 is spectacular. Colliding with an atom, it knocks out a new photon. Joining forces, the two photons knock out two more. Ultimately, for every photon entering the ruby, thousands more are released. Thus, the power of the signal is amplified by 10,000 to 1 (40 decibels).

Later we shall discuss the factors that make this amplifier almost noise-free. For the time being, we are concerned only with observing the nature of maser action itself. In the next chapter we shall move into the optical maser or laser. Meanwhile we again summarize the three basic keys as they are embodied in the ruby maser.

Key No. 1: By applying a magnetic field, we produce energy levels at microwave frequencies of convenient values.

Key No. 2: The population is inverted by "pumping in" energy by means of a microwave generator; the effect is enhanced by cooling the crystal to liquid helium temperature.

Key No. 3: The action is intensified by slowing down the photons as they move through the ruby; this prolongs the interaction between the photons and the excited atoms so that more of them can contribute energy, thereby producing strong amplification.

9 | RUBY LASERS AND HELIUM-NEON LASERS

The first laser · Solution of the resonance problem by means of parallel mirrors · The production of laser action in the ruby by harnessing the activity of orbital electron-magnets · How two gases, caused to work in partnership, made possible the first laser able to produce a continuous beam

Once the maser had been invented, it appeared probable, from general theoretical considerations, that the principle could be applied at higher frequencies. Among the goals present in the minds of the original maser pioneers was to make an oscillator at submillimeter wavelengths (from 0.1 to 1.00 millimeter). Instead, because it was the more feasible thing to do, they made their maser work at microwavelengths. However, now that the maser principle had been practically demonstrated, would it be possible to nudge it along to submillimeter waves?

Again a bird in the hand proved to be worth more than two in the bush. Little instrumentation existed for handling waves in the submillimeter region; nor were the spectra of materials in this region very well known. In contrast, the spectra of materials at the much higher optical frequencies had been extensively explored and were very well known. So it came to pass

113

that instead of modestly creeping along from micro-waves to submillimeter waves, maser research took a giant stride up the spectrum to wavelengths of the order of hundred thousandths of a centimeter.

It was seen from spectroscopic data that both solids and gases could be applied. But first a cardinal prob-lem would have to be solved—that of intensifying the action. In the ammonia maser the action is inten-sified by staging it in a resonant cavity, and in the ruby maser amplifier by retarding the signal so that it moves relatively slowly through the active medium. No such techniques were applicable at the extremely short wavelengths of light for which a conventional resonant cavity would have to be a small fraction of a centimeter.

The solution, it now appears in retrospect, was delightfully simple—a different kind of resonant cav-ity. Essentially, a cavity is resonant when it favors the buildup of energy at a particular wavelength and strongly resists the intrusion of other wavelengths. In general a cavity is caused to resonate by making its dimensions small integral multiples of the wave-length. It happens that resonance can also be secured by making waves travel back and forth between paral-lel reflectors. If the degree of parallelism is made sufficiently exact, resonance can be achieved at opti-cal wavelengths.

THE RUBY LASER

It was worked out in theory that a laser could be made by setting up an active medium between parallel mirrors and then exciting the medium in some suitable way. About two years later the basic concepts materialized in the first laser. Interestingly, its creator again chose the ruby as the active medium, drawing upon the same centers of magnetic activity in the crystal that made possible the ruby maser. This action, which we shall now try to describe, again illustrates our growing knowledge of the minute mechanisms of matter as well as our growing ability to control and apply them.

The action of the ruby laser is like that of the ruby maser in that in both we inject photons so as to raise chromium atoms up their energy ladder, then arrange for them to produce the amplifying action during their return to ground level. But whereas in the ruby maser we apply a magnetic field to create an energy ladder having rungs at the microwave frequencies we wish to work at, here we apply no field at all; instead we harness the natural levels of the few chromium atoms residing in the crystal.

The chromium atom's natural levels (modified, of course, by their crystalline surroundings) come into play when we cause a ruby to fluoresce. In this phenomenon, as mentioned earlier, the chromium atoms are raised up the ladder by the injection of high-energy photons such as those of ultraviolet. The atom then descends the ladder, and, between a specific level and the ground level, it emits red light.

The action that takes place in the ruby to produce this phenomenon centers in the same three magnetically unpaired electrons which produce microwave action. Only now, this trio is called upon to deal with optical photons which are tens of thousands of times more energetic than microwave photons. To accommodate microwave photons the three electrons had merely to swing through an angle. To absorb the relatively high energy of optical photons the atom's orbital system must respond in a markedly different manner.

We saw that when atoms come together to form molecules, the electrons in the outer orbits of atoms must move so as to adapt to the forces exerted by neighboring atoms. Because of the manner in which the chromium atom is bonded to its neighbors aluminum and oxygen, the three electrons are constrained to move in the general contour of a clover leaf (Figure 13). The orientation of this orbit is a measure of its energy. When we excite the system by injecting an optical photon, the orientation changes.

The exact effect on the orbit depends on the frequency of the exciting photon. The effect of the absorption of a violet photon (such as might be employed to pump a ruby laser) is to cause the orbit to swing

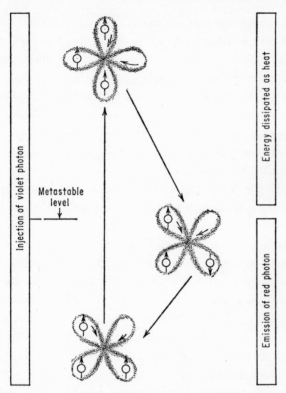

FIG. 13 Action of the three orbital electrons involved in ruby laser action. Just as hydrogen's single electron may appear to an observer to form a spherical cloud, so the three electrons exist in a clover-leaf cloud. When a violet photon is absorbed, the cloud may appear to swivel through an angle of 45°. Then, as the energy drops to the metastable level, the clover leaf swings back to its original position; at the same time, one of the electron-magnets flips through 180°.

as a whole through an angle of 45°, to occupy a new orientation corresponding to the higher energy level. The orbital system is now unstable, and like a bent spring, it almost instantly snaps back, releasing energy. Yet the atom does not at once return to the ground level. Instead, it "shifts gears," calling into action another kind of energy-storing mechanism that arises from the magnetic interplay among the three spinning electron-magnets.

We see from Figure 13 that when the atom is at ground level, all three electron-magnets point in the same direction. We see, too, that when the atom absorbs a violet photon and rises in energy, there is no change whatsoever in the direction of the magnets. Now as the atom works to rid itself of the excess energy, snapping the orbit back into its original orientation, at the same time one of the magnets flips through 180°. As a result, instead of descending directly to ground level, the atom lands at an intermediate level. In this first portion of its descent, the atom gives off excess energy as vibrations of the crystal lattice, that is, as heat. It is in the subsequent descent to ground level that it radiates fluorescent red.

Upon reaching the intermediate level the mechanism takes a rest, so to speak, pausing for $3/1,000$ second before the magnet flips back through 180°, returning the atom to ground level. This pause is of crucial importance to laser action. For though it may appear as an exceedingly short time, it is a long time when viewed against the swiftly changing scene in the crystal—so long that spectroscopists named this intermediate level the *metastable* (that is, *almost stable*) level. As a result of this slowed-down action, and provided there is a sufficient supply of excited atoms, the population inverts, making available enormous numbers of excited atoms capable of amplifying red light.

The basic features of a ruby laser are shown in Figure 14. The crystal is excited by an intense flash of light that pours in immense numbers of exciting violet and green photons which, in turn, cause the metastable level to become sufficiently overpopulated

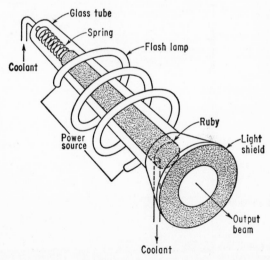

FIG. 14 Ruby laser (pulsed). (*Reprinted with permission. Copyright © 1961 by Scientific American, Inc. All rights reserved.*)

to produce the amplification of red light (Figure 15).

The ruby is formed in the shape of a cylindrical rod with ends made into mirrors whose surfaces are perpendicular to the long axis of the rod. A photon (Figure 16) that gets started along the axis of the rod is reflected at either end. Like speed swimmers racing to and fro between the ends of a swimming pool, the photons are reflected back and forth many thousands of times in each fraction of a second. In each lap they knock out new photons, and the action cascades to produce an intense flash of red light. If one of the mirrors is made slightly transparent, part of the light is transmitted through it in the form of a beam.

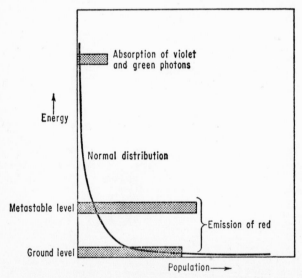

FIG. 15 Population inversion in ruby laser action.

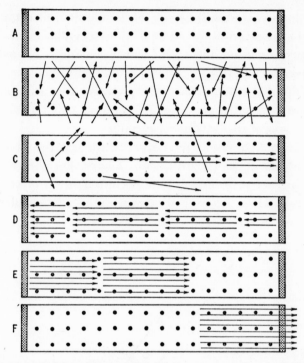

FIG. 16 Buildup of laser action: (*A*) Atoms are mostly unexcited, in ground state. (*B*) Excited atoms emit photons in all directions. (*C*) Photons that happen to get started along the axis are reflected by end mirrors. (*D*) *and* (*E*) Action builds up through thousands of reflections. (*F*) The laser beam emerges through the partially silvered surface. (*Reprinted with permission. Copyright © 1961 by Scientific American, Inc. All rights reserved.*)

Figure 17 shows a more efficient system of excitation based on a special optical system that concentrates light on the ruby, which, having a funnel-shaped end, further concentrates the illumination. With this scheme the laser produces a continuous stream of radiation although its power is but a small fraction of that attainable in pulses.

Laser light has a special quality, the nature and advantages of which are discussed later. For the time being, we wish only to note the mechanisms of laser action. Here, before carrying on to the next chapter, we again reiterate the three basic keys.

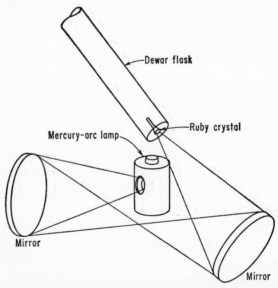

FIG. 17 Pumping arrangement in the first continuously operating ruby laser. Light from the arc is efficiently concentrated on the ruby crystal which is prevented from overheating by the cooling chamber.

Key No. 1: The ruby reacts energetically to red light so it can be used to amplify such light.

Key No. 2: The population is inverted by pumping in energy at a high point of the energy ladder.

Key No. 3: The action is intensified into a cascade by arranging for the photons to retrace their path through the crystal over and over again.

THE GAS LASER

It was natural for the laser pioneers to look hopefully to gases because many gases display two characteristics needed for efficient laser action: strong, sharp, spectral lines, and markedly unequal emission delays at different energy levels. A cardinal problem was that of devising a way to pump in sufficient energy to produce a workable population inversion.

In the first gas laser the problem was solved by using not one gas but two in a scheme which again illustrates how atomic energy ladders can be manipulated. The two gases helium and neon were caused to work in an ingeniously contrived partnership by which one gas did the energizing while the other did the amplifying. This was done by applying a curious property of helium long known to spectroscopists. A helium atom, when loaded with energy to one particular level on its ladder which we denote by X, cannot lose this energy by radiation. It can lose it in only one way—by collision with another atom which also has an X level in its energy ladder, and

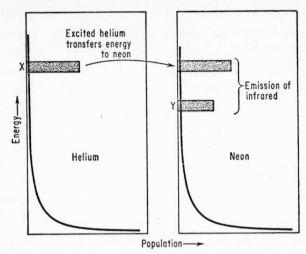

FIG. 18 Action in the helium-neon laser. Excited helium transfers energy to neon, causing a population inversion in neon and the emission of $\frac{1}{100}$ watt of infrared power at 1.1×10^{-4} centimeter wavelength or 2.7×10^{14} cps frequency.

which level is unoccupied. Neon has such an X level (Figure 18). When an excited helium collides with a quiescent neon atom, the helium's energy moves across to occupy the neon atom. To unload the energy, the neon drops to a level which we denote as the Y level. In doing so, it radiates infrared. Furthermore, there is a relatively long delay before the drop.

In this gas laser a large proportion of helium is mixed with a small proportion of neon (in a ratio of about 10 to 1), and the mixture is exposed to an ionizing radio-frequency voltage. This pushes a great many helium atoms far up their energy ladders. They promptly slip down to the X level where they stop, unable to lose energy except through collision. Very soon, however, the helium atoms collide with neon atoms—in turn raising them to the X level. Because there is a delay, neon atoms tend to pile up at the X level. This results in more neon atoms at the X level than at the Y level—the essential condition for amplifying infrared. Again, as in the ruby laser, the action is intensified by staging the action in a tube with reflecting ends, at least one of which is made slightly transparent to let the radiation emerge as a beam (Figure 19).

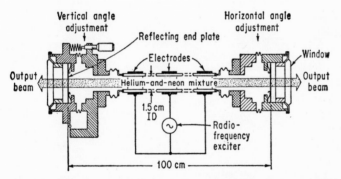

FIG. 19 Helium-neon laser. The action depends critically on extreme degree of parallelism between the end reflectors, which, furthermore, need to be flat to within a few wavelengths. Gas lasers using pure neon, xenon, krypton, argon, and various mixtures, together with various means of excitation, have produced wavelengths from 5.94×10^{-5} centimeter in the yellow to 3.45×10^{-3} centimeter in the far infrared.

10 | SEMICONDUCTOR-JUNCTION LASERS

The semiconductor-junction laser · Discussion of electrical conductivity in insulators, conductors, and semiconductors · How the p-n junction arises in the union of p and n semiconductors · How the junction which gives rise to the transistor and solar cell also produces laser action · Some advantages of the junction laser

In the immense variety of materials, in the numerous forms of energy and internal mechanisms as well as in the multiplicity of ways in which nature brings them together, the laser principle has a fertile field for new applications. Within four years of the advent of the laser, the principle had already invaded a field made famous by the solid-state diode, the silicon solar cell, and the transistor—that of the semiconductor junction.

In theory this was no surprise; the possibility of staging laser action in a semiconductor junction is implicit in its properties. To understand why, let us first look at some of the features that distinguish semiconductors from ordinary conductors and from insulators.

We know that insulators such as glass convey electric charge scarcely at all while conductors such as copper carry it in abundance. Between conductors and insulators there is an intermediate class known as semiconductors; they insulate much less than insulators and conduct much less than conductors.

In discussing the goings-on in a copper wire, we observed that the conduction of electricity is not like pouring water into an empty pipe; rather it is like pushing water into a pipe that is already full of water. Analogously, a material can convey electric charge only because it already contains electric charges that are movable. Why do some materials have movable charges while others do not? Again, we must look for the answer to the atoms of which they are constructed, particularly to the manner of their bonding.

Consider, for example, how copper atoms become bonded to form copper metal. In a copper atom there are 29 orbital electrons whose combined negative charge exactly balances the positive charge on the nucleus. But a copper atom has in its outermost orbit an electron that is precariously anchored; it readily becomes detached and wanders away. Lacking an electron, the atom, now electrically unbalanced, becomes a positive *ion*. To a free electron an ion appears as a positive charge, to which it is strongly attracted. Thus we have at work in the crystal strong attractive forces that tend to draw the ions and free electrons together. At the same time, we have counterbalancing forces consisting of the mutual repulsion between ions and between electrons. The opposed forces engage in a complex tug that causes the ions to organize into the cubical structure typical of the copper crystal. Meanwhile, the free electrons take on the additional task of providing enormous numbers of so-called *conduction* electrons which endow copper with its high conductivity.

There is another type of bonding, one in which electrons do not break away. Instead, an electron in one atom teams up with an electron in an adjacent atom. The negatively charged bonding electrons move with respect to each other and their parent positive nuclei so as to set up net attractive forces between the atoms. Meanwhile, the paired electrons continue as parts of the atoms and in no way contribute to conductivity. This type of bonding occurs in the crystalline substance germanium. The germanium atom has four bonding electrons. Each electron pairs off with an electron in an adjacent atom so as to form the rigid structure of the crystal. Again, every electron in every atom remains part of the atom; it is exclusively occupied in the bonding function and is not free to move about conducting charge. Pure germanium, therefore, is an insulator.

The phenomenon of semiconductivity is caused by minute defects in the germanium's structure just as both the color and the magnetic properties of the ruby are caused by minute defects in the structure of corundum. In germanium, such a defect may be produced by removing here and there a germanium atom and replacing it by one of arsenic. An arsenic atom has five bonding electrons. When we put such an atom into position, four of its electrons reach out and form partnerships with the four electrons available in the neighboring germanium atoms. Arsenic's fifth electron, however, having no electron to latch onto, becomes a free electron, which can engage in the process of conducting electric current.

If, instead of arsenic, we insert boron atoms, we produce an opposite result, for boron has only three bonding electrons. When we insert it in the germanium structure, the three bonding electrons reach out to join forces with three electrons in adjacent germanium atoms. But since the germanium atom has four electrons, one of them is left unpaired. Where an electron should be, there is a vacancy which is known as a *hole*.

Holes are securely anchored in atoms and so can't actually move around. Since they represent the absence of negative charges, they act as positive ones, tending to attract bonding electrons away from neighboring atoms. Holes and electrons "play a game." An electron can hop out of an atom and into a hole in another atom, leaving behind a hole which may, in turn, draw an electron from still another atom. In this way, billions of electrons can atom-hop through billions of atoms from one end of the crystal to the other. An imaginary observer of this process would see the electrons traveling in one direction and holes apparently traveling in the opposite direction. Physicists speak as easily of a hole current as they do of an electron current.

For those of us to whom the hole concept seems unreal and farfetched, it may help to consider the analogy of an audience moving through an auditorium in which the preferred seats are up front. The auditorium is full, and no one is allowed to enter until there is a vacant seat. As soon as a vacancy occurs, an individual is allowed to move in and occupy it. As the front seats are vacated people move up from the back of the auditorium to occupy them, thus creating more vacancies in the rear, which, in turn, are immediately filled. Thus, there is a constant motion of people through the auditorium in one direction while a stream of vacant seats travels in the opposite direction.

Semiconductors that conduct by means of free electrons are known as the n type while those that conduct by means of holes are of the p type. Each type can be produced at will by "doping" the crystal, as it grows, with a suitable impurity. The growing process can also be controlled to make one section n type and an adjacent section p type. The region in which the two types abruptly meet is known as a p-n junction.

In the $\frac{1}{10,000}$-inch-thick space in which the p and n materials are brought face to face occur those unique phenomena which make possible the semiconductor diode, the transistor, and the solar cell.

Whole books have been devoted to the laws, properties, and potentialities of the p-n junction. Here we
are concerned only with the junction in its roles as
an absorber and emitter of radiation.

Once the junction had been discovered (an event
that occurred in the 1930s) it was soon evident that,
on exposure to light, the junction generates electric
current. Following the invention of the transistor and
the development of junction theory, the phenomenon
was harnessed in the silicon solar cell, which converts
sunlight into small but useful amounts of electric
current. Given a sufficient number of cells, we can
generate a current powerful enough to activate telephone circuits and amplifiers in space vehicles. The
action of the silicon solar cell comes out of the relationship between photons of light and two particular
energy levels that prevail in a semiconductor.

The energies that may be possessed by electrons
in semiconductors can be just as firmly predicted by
quantum theory as they are determined among an
atom's orbital electrons. Also, as with orbital electrons, the energy can change only by jumping from
one allowable value to another. Here, particularly,
we are involved with the energy of a free electron in
n material and that of a hole in the p material. It
happens that a free electron possesses more energy
than does a hole. Hence, when an electron slips into
a hole, it can do so only by giving off energy. Conversely, when an electron jumps out of an atom, it

can do so only by acquiring additional energy. In making the transition from one energy to another, the electron may emit or absorb a photon at an optical frequency. Basically, this is the secret of both the solar cell and the junction laser.

In the junction of a solar cell (which is designed and proportioned for an optimum absorption of light), the free electrons of the n material are brought face to face with the holes of the p material. Impinging on atoms, light photons eject electrons and produce holes. This upsets the balance in the junction, creating a pressure which pushes electrons into the n side of the junction while holes are pushed into the p side. Thus, the two sides of the junction tend to become charged like the negative and positive terminals of a battery (a single silicon cell produces about 0.6 volts). When the two sides are connected by a wire circuit, a current flows.

This light-injection process is reversed in the junction laser. Injected into the n material by a suitable power source, electrons are pushed into the junction, where they encounter holes which, incidentally, are also in the process of being pushed toward the junction from the positive side of the power source. Combining with the holes, the electrons lose energy. In some crystals such as germanium, this loss is complicated by some of the lost energy appearing as heat motion of the crystal lattice and the remainder as a photon. But in certain other crystals, exemplified by gallium arsenide, there is a clear-cut transition in which the loss appears directly as a radiation photon. It is these emitted photons which provide the means for laser action.

In a junction laser (Figure 20), electrons injected into the junction produce an abundance of photons. The action builds up as photons striking electrons stimulate them to emit their excess energy as additional photons. To build it up still further, the end surfaces of the junction are polished to reflect. As in

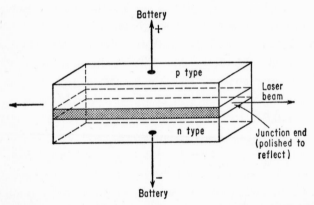

FIG. 20 In a p-n junction laser, action is produced by forcing electrons from the n region into the junction, while, in counterbalancing action, "holes" are forced in from the p region. In the junction, electrons combine with lower-energy holes, losing energy in the form of photons which in turn impinge on other higher-energy electrons and stimulate them to release additional photons. The action is intensified by making two opposite sides of the junction parallel and reflective. Actual thickness of the junction is about $\frac{1}{10,000}$ inch. Very high current densities are required to trigger laser action. For example, a gallium arsenide junction requires a minimum of about 10,000 amperes per square centimeter.

the ruby and gas masers, the action surges into a cascade.

The semiconductor laser has the big advantage that it does not require a separate auxiliary "pump," the active medium being excited by the direct injection of electrons. It is extremely efficient, being capable of transforming almost 100 per cent of the input power into radiation. Another prime advantage is that the frequency of the output radiation can be changed by controlling the chemical composition of the semiconductor; it can also be changed by altering the temperature. Meanwhile, the output power is readily controlled by changing the pump current.

So far, it has been our purpose to explain how atoms may be harnessed to amplify radiation and to point up those common principles by which masers and lasers are governed. This we have done by drawing attention to five pioneer types of devices created during what might be called the "early classical" period. Today, with hundreds of institutions and industrial concerns working in the field, it is reliably estimated that new laser materials, gas, liquid, and solid, will be appearing at a rate of one a month. Probably new laser types will proliferate with the abundance that has marked the growth of the electron tube. Here, we end our discussion of the internal mechanisms of masers and lasers and turn to a consideration of what the devices can do for us in science and technology.

11 | WAVES AND WAVE MOTIONS

What we need to know about waves to appreciate masers and lasers · All sound, radio, light, and all communications depend inevitably on wave action · How wave motions add to form complex patterns while the individual rhythms continue to be distinguishable · Fourier's theorem · The sine wave or frequency as the "atom" of the world of vibration

A laser is a maker and amplifier of electromagnetic vibrations. The mark of its performance, therefore, and the focus of our attention, lies in the character—the energy and shape—of the waves in which it deals. To help us think about what a laser does with waves, let us first refresh our memories with some facts about waves themselves—not an extensive incursion into the varied and wonderful world of waves but only a brief review of those few basic characteristics which are shared by all waves regardless of their type and which can help us appreciate the laser's peculiar qualities.

We observed earlier that physicists, in their consideration of radiation, have two hats: a photon hat and a wave hat. To understand how energy is withdrawn from excited atoms in order to bring about amplification, we found it expedient to think in terms of photons. Now we shall change hats and think of waves in the conventional way as wiggly curves in space or time.

This puts us on comfortably familiar ground, for wave motion—cyclic action—is something we intuitively grasp. It could not be otherwise, since perhaps nothing is more a part of our daily lives than cyclic activity. The world in which we exist is cyclic—a world in which day invariably follows night, spring always follows winter, and in which we could not survive at all without the physiological cycles pertaining to the heart, breath, appetite and sleep—indeed, we could not even read these words without the electric waves that endlessly course to and fro through our brains. A noncyclic world in which the same pattern of familiar events did not keep recurring over and over again would be not merely unthinkable but also unlivable.

Cyclic activity is just as inescapable in the propagation and movement of a disturbance from one place to another, for the only way in which solids, liquids, gases, and even "empty" space can propagate a disturbance is in the form of a cyclic motion. To talk to you, we must send a cyclic motion of sound through the air. To telephone you, we must generate and transmit a cyclic motion in electromagnetic energy. To illuminate you, we must send the cyclic motion which is light.

Paradoxically, as obvious as is the importance of wave activity in our lives, the motion itself is nearly always hidden. The wave motions of heat, light, electricity, and sound can become known to us only indirectly through their effects on our bodily senses and chemistry. The wave motions of radio, telephone, and television are known to us only when they are converted into sounds or pictures by our home sets. Nevertheless, there are a few wave motions that we directly experience, and from these we can perceive the basic characteristics of all waves, including the waves of the telephone, radio, and laser.

We can observe the elemental properties of waves by watching water waves as we sit in a rowboat gently rocked by a ground swell. Presently, a speedboat goes bouncing by. The speedboat generates a new set of waves which travel to us across the surface. Soon our boat is moving under the combined effects of two motions: the slow rhythm of the ground swell added to the faster rhythm from the speedboat. Complex as may be the motion of our boat, we can neverthe-less clearly detect the individual presence of each rhythm.

As the water waves show us, when waves of differ-ent rhythms come together, their motions are added. Yet each rhythm continues its individual existence as though it were alone (Figure 21). Conversely, a complex vibration breaks down into simpler vibra-tions. What our muscular senses tell us about water waves, our hearing tells us about sound waves. From the complex motion produced in our eardrums by an orchestra's sounds, we are able to pick out numerous individual tones. At the turn of the eighteenth century these properties of waves were expressed in a theorem by the French mathematician, Joseph Fourier.

Studying the nature of complex curves, Fourier discovered that he could construct any curve or graph whatsoever by merely adding together a sufficient number of undulating lines known as *simple harmonic curves*. His findings, called *Fourier's theorem,* apply equally to any wavy line—the outline of hills and valleys of a landscape, the vicissitudes of a sales chart, the progress (or retrogression) of a golf score, or the ups and downs of the stock market.

Fourier's theorem at once applies to sound vibrations, for a simple harmonic motion of the air is a

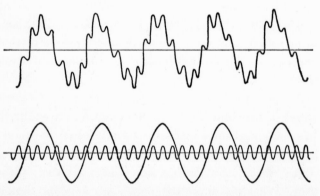

FIG. 21 Diagram showing superposition of wave motions in linear (nondistorting) medium.

pure tone. Fourier's theorem tells us (and experiment verifies) that a complex sound vibration consists at each instant of its existence of specific combinations of coexistent, pure tones (albeit the combination may change from moment to moment).

Generally, Fourier's theorem expresses the fact that all complex vibrations, of whatever type and in whatever medium, are reducible to what is known as *simple sinusoidal vibrations,* which we, for brevity, shall refer to as *sine waves.* When we dismantle a complex vibration, we do so, step by step, piece by piece, until we have broken down all its components into sine vibrations. Beyond this we cannot go, for the sine vibration is unanalyzable; it is the "atom" of the vibrating world; you can destroy it, but you cannot reduce it to something simpler and still have periodic motion.

These elementary components of all electromagnetic vibrations are thought of by communications engineers as *frequencies* while spectroscopists think of them as *wavelengths.* In considering a complex waveform, they speak of a range of *frequencies* or *wavelengths.* In what follows in this book it will help us to think of all waves, however complex, as simply aggregations of sine waves or frequencies.

An absolutely pure sine-wave vibration—like Plato's ideal geometric figures—is a concept that is never found individually embodied in nature. The wave motions we encounter in nature are complex. The wave outputs of generators, natural or man-made, inevitably consist of a group (or groups) of coexistent sine waves or frequencies. In the next chapter we compare the wave output of a laser with those of other generators.

12 | ELECTROMAGNETIC-WAVE GENERATORS

The comparative outputs of wave generators, natural or man-made · The wide continuous frequency band of incandescent solids versus the spectral lines of hot vapors · Radio transmitters produce single "spectral lines" · The radio transmitter's wave output is coherent · Why the laser's output is, at the same time, intense, coherent, and extremely directional · Laser light compared with sunlight

Electromagnetic-wave generators differ from each other in the frequency position of their outputs in the overall spectrum and in the width of the band or bands of frequencies they cover. Broadly, however, all may be thought of as falling in one of two classes. The first class, known as *blackbody* radiators, consisting of incandescent solids and exemplified by our sun, contain immense numbers of infinitesimal oscillators radiating at different frequencies. Under the agitation of heat, these oscillators join in producing, in unbroken sequence, the wide frequency range extending from ultraviolet to infrared, as shown in Figure 22.

The second class of wave generators—exemplified by flames, electrical sparks, and hot vapors—emit in a number of very narrow bands of frequencies known in spectroscopy as *spectral lines*. The triode and klystron oscillators of radio may be thought of as falling within this class, since they produce single "spectral lines" at radio frequencies.

Although a wave generator never produces a single frequency but rather one or more continuous bands of frequencies, these bands may be so narrow that for practical purposes they are thought of as single frequencies. Thus, light produced in a very narrow band of frequencies is thought of as *monochromatic,* or single-color. A radio station is spoken of as transmitting at a specific frequency even though this is only approximately accurate.

Thus, in producing spectral lines a wave generator such as a hot vapor is like a radio transmitting station. There is, however, a crucial characteristic in which they radically differ. The radiation put out by the radio station's antenna comes from a single oscillator that generates continuously. To simulate the hot

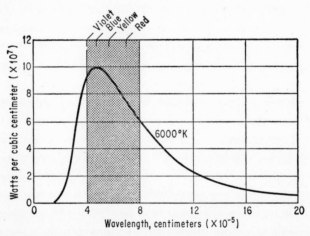

FIG. 22 The sun's spectrum, that of an incandescent solid, is a continuous spectrum, unlike that of a gas or electric spark.

vapor producing its spectral lines, you need to have the antenna fed by a great number of oscillators which emit randomly in spurts. As a result, while the wave-form from the radio transmitter is coherent and predictable, the waveform from the hot vapor is incoherent and unpredictable. This is because the waves from the individual uncoordinated oscillators, even though they may be of the same frequency, combine in or out of step in an infinite number of possible ways.

A laser organizes the radiation output from atoms so that it behaves like the output of a single oscillator. Basically, this organization is possible because the emitted radiation strictly obeys the stimulating radiation. The wave train emitted by a stimulated atom takes off in exactly the same direction, at exactly the same frequency, and exactly in step with a stimulating wave train; the two wave trains reinforce each other without any alteration in either frequency or direction.

If the direction in which the stimulating photon gets started happens to be at some angle to the axis of a laser's ruby or tube of gas, the photons in this direction of motion will eventually leave the crystal and be lost (Figure 16). However, the photons that get started in the direction of the axis are reflected by the mirrors. Racing to and fro along the axis, they encounter ever more charged-up atoms releasing more wave trains just like their own and always exactly in step. Joining forces, the sine-wave outputs of billions of atoms move out of the laser like a regiment of soldiers in step.

Contrasted with the light from an ordinary source such as an electric lamp, which radiates in almost every direction, the emergent light of the laser is extremely directional. In order to concentrate ordinary lamp light into a beam, it is necessary to employ reflectors and lenses. Laser light, because of the way it is generated, automatically emerges as a beam with such nearly parallel sides that (in a gas laser) it may enlarge less than 5 inches per mile.

Laser light is limited to an extremely narrow frequency range. Typically, the light from a ruby laser ranges from 400,000,000,000,000, to 400,006,000,000,-000 cps. Even narrower is the frequency band of a visible gas maser, which may range from 474,000,-000,000,000 to 474,000,000,600,000 cps and thus comes within two parts in a billion of being a pure sine wave—a degree of purity hundreds of thousands of times greater than that of a klystron, for instance.

Laser light achieves unprecedented intensity, surpassing (within its narrow frequency domain) even that of the sun. Incidentally, the fact that laser light surpasses that of the sun in intensity may not be so surprising when you consider how laser action is obtained by charging up the same or like atoms over and over again, and by projecting the released photons always along the same axis of the same narrow beam—and when you consider how, in comparison, the sun, despite its variety of atomic activity, huge energy, and wide frequency range, devotes but a small part of its atoms to producing the narrow range of frequencies involved in the laser—and how, furthermore, the sun spreads the radiation by projecting it in every possible direction. To help us appreciate the peculiar nature and intensity of laser light, Figure 23 shows the radiation emitted by the sun's surface from an area equal to about that of a representative ruby rod (1 square centimeter in cross section).

The sun's total radiation output at all frequencies

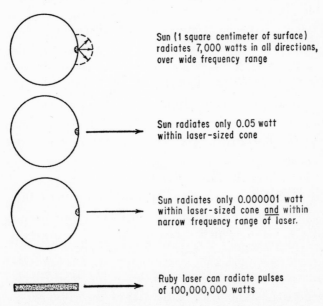

Sun (1 square centimeter of surface) radiates 7,000 watts in all directions, over wide frequency range

Sun radiates only 0.05 watt within laser–sized cone

Sun radiates only 0.000001 watt within laser–sized cone and within narrow frequency range of laser.

Ruby laser can radiate pulses of 100,000,000 watts

FIG. 23 Laser light's intensity compared with that of the sun.

(Figure 22) is 7,000 watts per square centimeter. The portion traveling along a laser-sized cone is only $\frac{5}{100}$ watt. Of this, the amount produced within the limited frequency range of a laser is only one-millionth of a watt. In comparison, the power in a ruby laser pulse can be made as large as 100 million watts during extremely short intervals of one-tenth of one-millionth of a second.

Could we match such intensity with ordinary sources —fires, flames, sparks, or incandescent bodies? In an ordinary source, intensity is a function of temperature. How hot would such a source have to be? Consider: The temperature of a kitchen gas flame is about 2700°C; that of an incandescent tungsten wire, 3000°C. The sun's surface temperature is about 6000°C. The temperature of a very hot star may be 100,000°C outside and 50,000,000°C inside. To match the intensity of powerful laser pulses, it would be necessary to attain a temperature of 10 million billion °C, which is hotter than anything known to exist in the entire cosmos.

How laser light can serve both science and technology will be covered later. Meanwhile, in the following chapter, we shall deal first with the contributions of the maser, which preceded the laser historically.

13 | MASER USES AND APPLICATIONS

How masers can be used to advantage in spectroscopy and time measurement and as low-noise amplifiers in the reception of weak signals in satellite communications · Discussion of reasons for vanishingly small internal noise in the ruby traveling-wave maser

The big achievement of the first (ammonia) maser was to demonstrate that the principle of stimulated emission could be applied in a practical device. However, in the variety of uses to which it might be put, the maser has been far outstripped by its glamorous descendent, the laser. Nevertheless, there are some ways in which the maser can be used to advantage as an oscillator, and there is one outstanding way in which it has been used as an amplifier.

First, as to the maser as an oscillator. In triode and klystron oscillators the frequency is determined by a tuned wire circuit or a tuned cavity, and it is therefore subject to variations caused by mechanical vibration, aging, and temperature changes. The ammonia maser (or one using some other gas or vapor) has the inherent advantage that its frequency is determined by the innate and virtually invariable vibration frequency of atoms or molecules.

The ammonia maser's constancy of oscillation can

be applied to the measurement of time, for we measure time by means of a periodic motion. In the grandfather's clock the periodic motion is supplied by a pendulum. In the household electric clock the "pendulum" is in the form of the 60-cycle alternating current of the power supply. In time and frequency standards much greater constancy is obtained by applying the vibrations of a crystal-controlled electron-tube oscillator.

Still more constant vibrations can be obtained by harnessing the natural oscillations of atoms or molecules. Here the maser provides oscillations which have a frequency variation of one part in 10 billion. Even greater precision is obtainable with another kind of maser utilizing an energy jump in the hydrogen atom. Such ultrapure oscillations can also be used to advantage in spectroscopy for measuring the emission and absorption spectra of materials at microwave frequencies.

As an amplifier the maser achieved success unparalleled by any other device. True, as a microwave amplifier for general commercial uses the maser is far too complicated to compete with such sophisticated devices as the klystron and traveling-wave tube. Yet there is one characteristic in which the traveling-wave ruby maser outstrips all its competition, and that is its vanishingly small internal noise. This characteristic permits the clear reception of extremely weak radio signals, a benefit of great value in an age when we seek to listen to satellites and pull in distant radio "whispers" from the far reaches of the universe.

The interference caused by noise in communications is something we are all only too familiar with in our world of sound. In a noisy room we may have to shout in order to be heard; for a whisper to be distinguishable there must be extreme quiet. Analogously, the radio "whispers" that come to us from outer space can be detected only in the presence of extreme radio quiet.

In radio reception incoming signals must compete with interfering vibrations from various sources, including radio transmitters other than the one we are listening to, atmospheric static, and man-made static from automobile ignition, power lines, and X-ray machines. Together these interfering vibrations can blot out the signal.

We can make a weak signal strong by amplifying it; but since the amplifier cannot tell the difference between the desired signal and the interference, it amplifies both equally. If, for example, the interfering waves are half as strong as the signal on entering the amplifier (and therefore a strong source of interference with the signal), they will still be half as strong when they leave, no matter how powerful the amplifier. Thus, the amplifier, with all its power, is helpless. *Solution:* Keep the interference out of the amplifier.

Fortunately, much of the interference can be kept

out through appropriate circuit design, strategically located wave filters, the type of modulation used, and directional antennas. Fortunately, too, at the microwave frequencies used in satellite communications, the atmospheric static that plagues our radiobroadcast receivers is almost nonexistent. A satellite microwave receiver can be designed to shut out externally caused interference so effectively that we are left only with the noise made by the amplifier itself.

In our home radios we hear this noise as a crackling hiss when we turn up the volume to pull in a weak station. Normally we aren't aware of this noise because most of the stations we listen to have a strong signal, and we don't have to turn up the amplification to hear them. In contrast with the 10-billion-to-1 amplification necessary in a satellite receiver, this noise would be as Niagara Falls is to the chirp of a cricket.

An electron-tube amplifier has a built-in noise-maker—the electron stream upon which the tube's action depends. This electron-stream noise occurs because the electrons originate randomly at different levels in the cathode's interior, and they consequently emerge from the cathode's surface at different speeds. As a result, the electron flow varies ever so slightly in density. In turn, these minute variations cause corresponding variations on the electric charge in the anode, which in turn generate noise vibrations.

The enormous advantage of the maser lies in that it has no electron stream to generate noise. The only noise is the thermal noise made by its own substance —the ruby with its encompassing wave guides and associated parts and components.

All matter makes noise because atoms and molecules, agitated by heat, generate vibrations which may vary randomly in frequency from 1,000 to 10 trillion cps. Thermal noise vibrations that fall within the operating frequency range of a maser are potential sources of interference. Minute though such interference would be in ordinary radio communications, it becomes a formidable enemy in the new science of satellite communications and radio astronomy.

Physicists think of thermal noise in terms of its origin—heat. Since the energy of the noise increases as the temperature (and consequently the heat agitation) increases, physicists find it convenient to express noise energy in terms of temperature—but they don't use the temperature scale that we are accustomed to use. Most of us think of a temperature as so many degrees F or C (Fahrenheit or Centigrade) above or below some arbitrary zero point. Physicists think of temperature as a measure of the vibrational energy of atoms and molecules. This energy reaches a theoretical minimum at a temperature of minus 273°C, which they define as *absolute zero;* they measure temperature from there on up in absolute degrees K (Kelvin). Thus, 0°C become 273°K, and room temperature becomes 293°K.

We may be intrigued to learn that the chairs on which we sit broadcast a 293°K noise. A deep-freeze refrigerator murmurs softly at 263°K, while a hot cathode shouts at 1000°K. Even the air makes a tiny amount of noise, which, however small, has nevertheless been measured. The volume of air "seen" on a dry day by a satellite antenna pointed vertically upward produces a 2.4°K whisper (at Telstar wavelengths).

In the Telstar ground receiver at Andover, Maine, a traveling-wave ruby maser helps bring in signals of an extraordinary minuteness. Located in rural terrain and sheltered by hills, this receiver is protected to a singular degree from man-made interference. The antenna is exceptionally directional: like a blinkered horse, it "sees" only what is directly ahead. About the only noise that accompanies the signals entering the antenna from outer space is that made by atomic and molecular oscillations in the particular section of atmosphere "seen" by the antenna.

Once in the receiver, the signal has only to cope with the noise generated by the receiver itself. Maintained at a temperature close to absolute zero, the ruby maser amplifier itself exists in near-perfect stillness, making a noise at 3.5°K only. This added to the noise contributed by the air, radome, antenna, connectors, waveguides, and other apparatus brings the total noise to about 32°K, which is to be compared to the 3000°K noise generated by a conventional microwave receiver.

The Telstar receiver can clearly detect a radio signal that has an energy of less than 10^{-14} watt. Here it is important to bear in mind that this figure 10^{-14} applies to a signal having a bandwidth of 25×10^6 cps—and the narrower the frequency band within which the signal is contained, the less the energy of the interfering noise; more precisely, the magnitude of the receivable signal decreases in proportion to the bandwidth.

By interposing filters to limit the bandwidth to that of a voice (say, 2,000 cps) it is possible to pull in a signal of only 10^{-18} watt, which is hundreds of millions of times smaller than can be picked up by a broadcast receiver. Yet, even this is not the limit of this receiver's sensitivity. With a bandwidth of only 1 cycle, as might be used in radio astronomy, the receivable signal is reduced to 10^{-21} watt, which is equal to one-thousandth of one-millionth of one-millionth of one-millionth of a watt.

14 | LASER USES AND APPLICATIONS

The laser's potentialities in science and technology are portrayed in terms of four basic categories · How the device offers advantages in welding, chemistry, spectroscopy, interplanetary signaling, radar, and communications

In the previous chapter, we observed some of the ways in which a maser can be employed to advantage as an oscillator and also as an amplifier. The laser, too, can be employed both as an oscillator and an amplifier, but to date it has been thought of primarily as an oscillator, able to project into space a beam of radiation of extraordinary purity and intensity. To appreciate the potentialities of a laser beam, let us note some basic ways in which we seek to apply radiation in science and technology.

1. To project intense energy into a small area to illuminate, melt, weld, perforate, or ignite; to induce specific chemical action

2. To determine the spectra of materials—the pattern of their absorption and transparency at different frequencies, or wavelengths

3. To determine the distance, velocity and direction as well as the size and form of distant objects by means of the reflected signals of radar

4. To transmit meaningful signals—sound, pictures, or data—from one point to another

In addition to being far more intense than light from ordinary sources, light from a laser can be more readily focused. The reasons are illustrated in Figure 24. Emerging from different points in its source, ordinary light enters a focusing lens at a variety of angles. This spreads the light, limiting the minimum size of the area into which it may be focused. In addi-

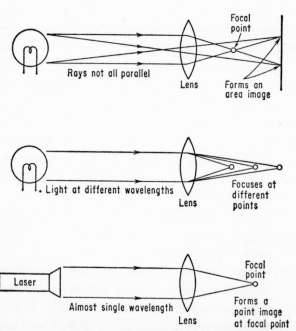

FIG. 24 Focusing characteristics of laser versus ordinary light. Laser light is readily focusable into a tiny space. (*Adapted from "Electronics."*)

tion, each of the different frequencies from an ordinary source, being differently refracted, comes to a focus at a different point along the axis of the lens. By contrast, laser light, entering the lens along parallel lines and being nearly of a single frequency, can be focused into a spot theoretically no wider than a wavelength of the light, or approximately $\frac{1}{10,000}$ centimeter.

The projection of intense energy in a small area can be applied to cut and punch metals and, in microwelding, to join extremely small parts without their being touched. It can provide the intense illumination (thousands of times brighter than sunlight) needed to photograph extremely fast moving objects in very short exposure intervals or to capture a view of materials in the instant of fracturing, melting, or exploding. Highly concentrated intense energy is applicable in surgery to eliminate even one cell from an infected area and, in cases of detached retina, to "weld" the retina back in position.

APPLICATIONS TO CHEMISTRY

Sharply focusable and nearly monochromatic, a laser beam offers attractive possibilities in the exploration of molecular structure and the nature of chemical reactions, the results of which could have important effects on chemical science. Usually, chemical reactions are set off by heat. Ingredients are poured together, and the mixture is shaken to cause a reaction. A laser beam provides a way to trigger a particular chemical reaction in mixtures capable of several reactions. Thus, a laser beam projected into a mixture of gases could cause a reaction in only one of the gases without disturbing the others, and in the absence of the smothering effects of excessive heat. In exploring compounds, it offers a means to pinpoint, and cause action in, one group of molecules rather than another.

THE LASER IN SPECTROSCOPY

In the phenomenon known as *Raman scattering,* a molecule struck by a photon may dispose of the energy in two ways. It may retain part of the energy, absorbing it into its electron system, and emit the remainder as a new photon. Since the new photon is of lower energy than the impinging photon, it is of lower frequency. Measurements of the frequency difference between the impinging and emitted radiation provide information about the vibrational and rotational states of molecules that cannot be obtained in other ways.

Here a laser beam provides the energetic radiation needed to produce scattered radiation strong enough to be reliably measured. In a special type of laser, stimulated Raman emission has been applied to produce laser light of several frequencies below that of the main operating frequency of the device. Thus, the powerful impact of a laser beam can be applied via Raman scattering to generate high-intensity laser light at many different frequencies.

SPACE AGE USES

One might think that a perfectly parallel beam of laser light projected into the heavens would continue on forever (provided nothing got in the way) without spreading out and thereby losing intensity. Actually, this happy situation can never occur because of the *diffractive* (breaking up) action which affects all light beams regardless of their origin or manner of projection.

Always a wavefront diffracts so that the beam diverges regardless of the angle into which the beam has been focused. Though by using a reflector or lens of wide diameter, the diffraction angle may be made extremely small, the result is still a gradual broadening of the beam. With a particular laser and optical system that can now be built, this broadening can be kept down to as little as 5 feet per thousand miles. A suitably focused laser beam can be made to deliver at a distant point an intensity of electromagnetic energy enormously greater than anything previously possible. This opens up some fascinating horizons.

POWER TRANSMISSION

We may think of a laser beam as a low-loss power-transmission line. With focusing lenses inserted at sufficient intervals and in the absence of the atmosphere, it would be theoretically possible to achieve a loss of only 0.05 per cent per 20 miles. An existing laser, it has been calculated, could be focused to heat a pot of coffee at a distance of 1,000 miles. At this time, however, an immense obstacle to using laser beams to convey bulk power is the problem of feeding in sufficient "pump" power. While the laser beam faces insuperable competition as a power carrier on earth, it may present attractive advantages in space. For example, if technology should make it possible, it might be advantageous to run a *laser power line* out to a satellite to operate low-power equipment.

SATELLITE NUDGING

Light exerts a tangible pressure. A laser beam, it has been demonstrated, exerts a pressure of several pounds per square inch, albeit over a tiny area. When a satellite begins to slow down and thus be drawn toward the earth, a laser beam projected from the earth may be used like a giant finger gently to prod it back into higher orbit.

INTERPLANETARY SIGNALING

Another use is to provide light signals that are visible to the naked eye or affect a photographic plate, after traveling over considerable distances, for example, to and from another planet. It has been calculated that 10,000 watts of light from a laser, focused and projected by a 200-inch reflector, would be visible through a 200-inch telescope, or be photographable, with a 1-minute exposure, at a distance of 10 light-years. Thus, it is possible to send laser light which can be detected at interstellar distances and be distinguishable from the background light of the stars.

RADAR

Laser light offers important benefits in radar which, by bouncing signals, seeks to determine the distance, speed, and direction of motion of distant objects as well as their size, shape, and superficial characteristics. Powerful laser pulses are capable of producing measurable reflections over greater distances than microwave radar. Also, the size of objects that can be discerned decreases with the wavelength. At the $\frac{1}{100,000}$-inch wavelength of light, radar can detect much smaller objects than can be done with inches-long microwaves. According to calculations, with transmitting and collector mirrors 2 feet wide and a 16-watt laser beam, the distance of an object 100 miles away is measurable to an accuracy of 1 part in 100,000.

There are also applications in the measurement of velocity. A radio beam reflected by a moving object returns to the transmitter slightly changed in frequency because of the so-called *Doppler shift,* a phenomenon we experience in the changing pitch of a whistle given off by a passing train. The velocity of the object (which is determined by the frequency change in the reflected waves) can be determined with greater accuracy at optical frequencies than at lower frequencies. Thus, a laser beam could be used for the precise determination of the velocity of satellites.

MEASURING THE VELOCITY OF LIGHT

Is the velocity of light invariably constant? Or are there circumstances in which it varies? The answer is of fundamental importance to our theories of how our universe is constructed and how it runs. With laser light it is possible to measure the velocity of light to a new order of accuracy.

This new accuracy has already been put to use in a repeat of the historic Michelson-Morley experiment, which was made many years ago to determine whether light travels in apparently empty space or is transported by an all-pervading ether.

If light is indeed transmitted by an ether, the velocity cannot be absolutely constant; it must be affected by the motion of the earth through space; it must be greater or less depending on the direction in which the light is aimed. Such a change in velocity must alter the time required for laser light to traverse the distance between the end mirrors and must result in a change in the frequency of the output beam.

To check the point, a group of experimenters have set up a laser in a wine cellar on Cape Cod, far removed from sources of vibration such as automobile traffic. When the weather is calm and the earth is quiet, the frequency of their laser beam is constant to within a few cycles in 100 trillion. With this degree of constancy, it is possible to detect changes in the velocity of light of $\frac{1}{10}$ inch per second.

HOW POWERFUL ARE LASERS?

In terms of power, lasers are divisible into two categories: continuous and pulsed. Continuously operating lasers are of feeble output; pulsed lasers achieve spectacular power for brief periods.

A continuously operating gas or ruby laser of present design produces only a few milliwatts. In contrast, a pulsed ruby laser can generate a 100-million-watt pulse, enough to burn a hole in steel. But this gigantic power endures for only a fraction of a millionth of a second. Having discharged its energy, the "pump" (like a pitcher before delivering his next pitch) must rest for a relatively long time as energy accumulates for the next pulse.

The production of continuous high power presents formidable problems. Whatever the type of laser involved and whatever new kinds of "pumps" future invention may create, the production of powerful laser outputs requires a means for pumping in great quantities of power, and that this be accomplished without burning up the active material.

To generate 100 million watts continuously, the pump (even assuming an unattainable 100 per cent efficiency) would need the capacity of the power plant of a city. With the less than 10 per cent efficiency currently attainable, the power plants of at least 10 cities would be required.

COMMUNICATIONS

Perhaps the particular potentiality of laser beams that has most stimulated the popular imagination lies in their theoretical ability to carry enormous amounts of simultaneous information. A laser beam is theoretically capable of simultaneously transporting the voices of five times the population of the United States.

The use of light itself to carry meaningful signals is no new thing, possibly dating back to the time when some early ancestor discovered that he could attract attention by flashing the glint of sunlight from a polished stone. Thousands of years later the sending of flashes of sunlight as coded signals became embodied in the heliograph. Nor is the use of light to carry speech a novelty. As mentioned before, as far back as the 1880s the telephone's inventor demonstrated the transmission of voice signals by means of focused light beams, and for many years now light has been employed to record sound on movie film and to reproduce it. The startling thing about laser light lies not in the fact that it can carry a voice but rather in the fantastic number of voices it might carry at the same time.

Over a long period of years we have had microwave systems in which focused beams transmit thousands of simultaneous voices. Broadly speaking, such systems are possible because we have a capable technology and because of the elementary fact that the waves can be effectively modulated—fashioned to carry information—for multivoice transmission. Hitherto, light of sufficient intensity for communications has been of a relatively wide frequency band, and it has been incoherent. By providing coherent narrow-band light waves like those used in radio, the laser makes it technically possible to modulate light as we now modulate radio waves. So, if we can develop the necessary technique, we can make light waves work like radio waves, as mass carriers of information.

If you happen to be acquainted with communications theory, the enormous traffic capacity inherent in a beam of light is at once obvious when the magnitude of the frequency is mentioned. But in case you are among those for whom that truth does not leap to mind immediately, we go on in the next chapter to point out some of the elementary reasons why it is possible at all to make waves share voices. Then, we shall try to indicate how laser light can join the world's rapidly growing parade of mass-information carriers.

15 SIMULTANEOUS MULTIVOICE TRANSMISSION

How voices can be made to share wire pairs or beams of waves by means of amplitude modulation · How voices may be stacked up in the spectrum · Why a wide frequency band is needed to carry many voices together

If we can see how a wire circuit or radio beam can share as few as two simultaneous voices without mutual interference, then it is just a matter of simple arithmetic to see why it is possible (given a physical system with suitable characteristics) to make them share a billion. Let us start out by observing the essential nature of the thing we require the telephone to transmit when we talk.

In talking we "write" words in the air; they travel to the ears of our listeners as meaningful patterns in pressure. Were a sensitive gauge held near a listening ear, the air pressure would be seen to rise and fall through a succession of hills and valleys hundreds of times a second. Each word, each sound has its own unique pressure pattern. This the eardrum records and the mind recognizes, and it is this pattern which all speech communications must take in, transport, and deliver.

Providing, therefore, we can succeed in delivering

the original pattern, we are free to dismantle it or otherwise manipulate it in any way we please. It is through such manipulation that many voices are fitted in with each other to travel over the same pair of wires at the same time. In one such technique known as *amplitude modulation* a voice pattern is transported by impressing it on a *carrier* vibration. Here, we single out this particular technique and consider it because, we believe, an understanding of how it works can most easily lead to an appreciation of the potentialities of laser light.

We know from Fourier's theorem that a voice pattern consists, at each instant of its existence, of a specific group of sine waves or frequencies. To deliver the voice undistorted it is necessary only to reproduce in a receiver, at each instant, the same sine waves, in their original phase relationship and relative strength.

To transmit by means of amplitude modulation the pattern is fed into a device known as a *modulator* in company with a sine-wave *carrier* vibration specially generated for the occasion. Virtually, a modulator is a special kind of vibration generator. It takes each component sine wave in the voice pattern and combines it with that of the carrier to produce two new sine waves. One of the new sine waves has a frequency equal to the sum of the frequency of the carrier wave and that of the voice sine wave, while the other new sine wave has a frequency equal to their difference. Thus, if we feed into a modulator a voice frequency of 256 cps along with a carrier frequency of 50,000 cps, the modulator reacts by producing two new frequencies—one the difference frequency at 49,744 cps and the other the sum frequency at 50,-256 cps.

Now we have translated the 256 frequency up the spectrum and have created two possible "stand-ins." [1] Either will suffice to transmit the frequency we want. In radiobroadcasting, both "stand-ins" are sent to conserve power; but in wire circuits, where frequency space is at a premium, one is usually suppressed.

Suppose that we suppress (by using wave filters) the difference frequency and also the 50,000-cps carrier frequency; we transmit only the 50,256-cps frequency. At the receiver, we have already a second 50,000-cps oscillator and a second modulator. In the modulator the incoming 50,256 cps combines with the 50,000 cps to produce 256 cps—the original frequency.

At each and every instant, the modulator does this with each and every frequency in a voice. Assuming that the voice frequencies to be picked up and delivered may be as low as a few cycles and as high as 4,000, we must be prepared, at each and every instant, to transmit an assortment of stand-in frequencies which may occur anywhere in a band extending from 50,000 to 54,000 cps.

We may send a second voice by modulating it with

---

[1] Actually these modulation products also *intermodulate,* but this need not concern us here.

the output of another oscillator at 54,000 cps. This second voice can be made to travel in the band ranging from 54,000 to 58,000 cps, an unoccupied range of frequencies in which it can exist as privately as though the first voice were nonexistent. Thus, we may send two voices simultaneously in the range from 50,-000 to 58,000 cps. Given a third oscillator at a third carrier frequency, we can send a third voice, along with the first two, in the range from 58,000 to 62,-000 cps.

Theoretically, we can translate voices and deposit them for transmission all over the spectrum. In practice, though, voices are usually allocated in groups to different parts of the frequency spectrum, strategically separated by empty spaces to prevent interference.

How far can you carry this process of relocating voices in the frequency spectrum? The answer depends on the frequency bandwidth of the system. This brings us to the battle of the bandwidth and to why the laser tantalizes communications science with the possibility of an overwhelming victory.

16 | THE BATTLE OF THE BANDWIDTH

The significance of frequency bandwidth · How communications science and technology have gradually increased bandwidth · Some milestones in the ascent to ever higher operating frequencies · The enormous bandwidth of laser light and how it might be applied

Although the term *frequency* band may be a stranger to our vocabulary, its effects are frequently and vividly experienced in our everyday world of sound. Particularly it enters into our enjoyment of music. Listening to an orchestra in an auditorium, we feel that we hear the sound fully and naturally. That's because there is no cutting off of essential frequencies, no distortion of the relative strength of the vibrations. Listening to the same orchestra through a closed door, or as it comes to us by way of a long narrow corridor, we may notice that the sounds are muffled and unnatural. That's because matter and the spaces it encloses are frequency-selective. Doors and corridors transmit unevenly at different frequencies, variously cutting off high or low notes while unnaturally accentuating others.

Similar limitations plague the electric counterparts of sound vibrations in electronic circuits. With radio sets and record players, we may be acutely conscious of the limitations imposed by inadequate bandwidth. While we are irritated by the tinny tones of a small radio whose diminutive speaker severely cuts off both the higher and lower frequencies, we are delighted by the rich natural sound of a hi-fi set specifically designed to transmit the full frequency band of orchestral music.

Although the limitations of frequency bandwidth may merely lessen our enjoyment of music, the telephone transmission engineer sees them as an obstacle to supplying long-distance communications at realistic cost. His cost incentive is easy to see when you consider that, in telephoning from my home to yours a few miles away, it is economical to devote to the job an individual pair of wires; but if your home is in a city thousands of miles away, it would be very costly to have my voice monopolize one very long pair of wires stretching all the way from me to you. For long distance it is more economical to connect me to a terminal, where my voice is sent over a wire pair or radio beam in company with many others, perhaps thousands of others.

The sending of many voices together demands efficient transmission over an adequate bandwidth, a far wider band than the 0 to 4,000 cps needed for a voice or the 0 to 15,000 cps needed for music. The attainment of wider bands comes by pushing up the operating frequency. When this occurs, wire circuits reduce the magnitude of electromagnetic waves by turning them into heat; the higher the frequencies, the greater the reduction. To make wires carry many voices at once, to achieve ever-wider usable bands, communication engineers must engage in a constant struggle with these high-frequency losses.

In this struggle, the communications engineer's goals contrast with those of his counterpart in electric power. While the telephone engineer and the electric power engineer both seek to accumulate energy in one place and send it to another and both employ electromagnetic waves, the electric power engineer is interested primarily in delivering bulk power to your home. To you as a consumer it is of no interest at what frequency the 500 watts needed to run your electric toaster vibrates, provided it toasts the toast. In contrast, the telephone engineer must figuratively make the delivered energy talk; to accomplish this he must use extraordinary finesse to manipulate milliwatts and microwatts of power over a great variety of frequencies and distances.

Broadly speaking, the developers of electric power generators and transmission systems have been finding ways to deliver bulk power over greater distances ever more efficiently, while the developers of telephony have (among other goals) struggled to transmit intelligence at ever-higher frequencies. By developing, perfecting, and putting together basic vibration-controlling elements—inductors, capacitors, resistors, filters, equalizers, amplifiers, thermistors, varistors, detectors, crystal frequency controls, rectifiers, and more recently crystal diodes and transistors—transmission technologists have steadily expanded wire and radio systems into still wider highways operating with high efficiency over frequency bands hundreds of thousands of times wider than that of the first telephone. To establish a work-a-day perspective in which to gauge the theoretical capabilities of laser light as a possible communications medium, we note here a few of the milestones which have marked the ascent to higher frequencies as it has occurred in the Bell System (Figure 25).

The practicality of the *carrier* technique was demonstrated in 1918 when the Bell System put into operation a system which transmitted four simultaneous voices over a pair of wires (the kind we see strung on telephone poles over the countryside). In the 1930s it became feasible to apply carrier techniques to cables, and in a particular system a pair of wires in a cable (where it exists with numerous other pairs) was made to work at up to 60,000 cps. The system is operated from a minimum of 12,000 cps to a maximum of 60,000 cps, thus providing a band 48,000 cps wide. It sends, over a wire pair—48,000 divided by 4,000—12 voices. At the same time it sends, in the same frequency band, 12 voices in the opposite direction over another and electrically separate wire pair.

Thus, the system handles 12 conversations over two wire pairs.

Later came the development of a type of conductor in which a wire runs coaxially along a pencil-sized metal tube. Far less destructive to high frequency, a *coaxial* conductor permits the economic realization

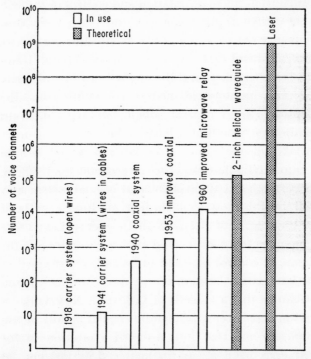

FIG. 25 Diagram showing the theoretical voice capacity of a laser beam compared with that of some existing communications media in the Bell System. A voice channel involves four conductors, two sending and two receiving; likewise, it involves two microwave beams and would involve two laser beams.

of a band up to 8,300,000 cps, providing for the simultaneous transmission of more than 1,800 conversations over two coaxials.

Now it may be you are thinking that this is pretty dull stuff compared with masers and lasers. Actually, though, a long-distance high-traffic telephone circuit results from the manipulation and control of the selfsame electromagnetic energy as does the laser. Most of us may not be aware of the extraordinarily precise energy control that had to be realized through transmission technology and the engineering arts to create the great highways of modern communication—the identical energy control, albeit employing different technology, would also have to be realized in order to take the laser out of the laboratory and fashion it into a reliable round-the-clock commercial system. In particular, a transcontinental coaxial system may well be the most sophisticated machine ever built for the control of electromagnetic energy. Let us take a moment to observe—and perhaps wonder at—the degree of control that had to be and was attained in the latest coaxial system now spanning our continent.

Assume that a voice is picked up in New York for transmission over a 3,200-mile coaxial circuit to San Francisco and that it is assigned a position in the frequency band at approximately 6,500,000 cps. At this frequency the cable loss is about 10 decibels per mile, corresponding to a reduction in power in the ratio of 10 to 1. At the end of 2 miles the reduction is 20 decibels, corresponding to a reduction of 100 to 1. At the end of 3,200 miles the total loss amounts to 32,000 decibels, which corresponds to a ratio of $10^{3,200}$ to 1 (the figure $10^{3,200}$ represents a number consisting of 1 followed by 3,200 zeros—enough to fill more than two pages of this book).

The cable loss is never allowed to get the upper hand. Every 4 miles the voice is sent through an amplifier that puts in compensating gain. In its journey from New York to San Francisco the voice passes through approximately 800 amplifiers which produce an aggregate gain of 32,000 decibels—a ratio of $10^{3,200}$ to 1.

In contrast to the enormous loss and amplification through which a voice must pass, the power of a voice itself is extraordinarily small. At New York the voice power fed into the system may be a pleasantly audible $\frac{1}{1,000}$ watt. This tiny power must be manipulated through a gain of $10^{3,200}$ in order to deliver a pleasantly audible voice in San Francisco.

It would be nice to adjust the total amplification so as to exactly balance the loss once and for all, and then leave it, as we do when we adjust the volume control of a radio receiver and then sit back and listen without having to make any further adjustment for hours. Actually, the balancing job is greatly complicated by the fact that the cable loss is not constant but varies with the cable temperature.

If the cable temperature decreases by only 1°F, the

total transcontinental cable loss would decrease by 40 decibels—in the ratio of 10,000 to 1. If no adjustment were made, our 1-milliwatt voice would zoom in at a level of 10 watts, high enough to damage amplifiers along the way and to be painful to the ear. Contrarily, an increase in cable temperature of 1°F would reduce 1 milliwatt to an inaudible one 10-millionth watt.

To control the gain at master control points along the route, the system has electronic "watchmen" which "keep an eye" on the temperature and automatically adjust the amplification to balance the loss. So precisely is this balance maintained that the 1-milliwatt voice which departed from New York arrives in San Francisco at an energy not greater than 1.26 milliwatts and not less than 0.974 milliwatt at any time of day or in any season.

Yet, this is not all. The system performs this balancing feat not just for one voice but for 1800 simultaneous voices with each (being in a different part of the frequency spectrum) subject to a different loss, and so requiring an individual amount of amplification.

Now, we have seen how, by pushing up the operating frequency of wire systems, it is possible to realize greater bandwidth and thus to carry more simultaneous voices. To achieve still greater bandwidth, transmission technology moved into space, harnessing radio beams.

Like wire systems, radio systems, too, have their particular limitations. Though space itself has an infinite bandwidth, restrictions are imposed by the limited bandwidth of the transmitter, receiver, antennas, amplifiers, modulators, and other apparatus components. There is the additional restriction that each radio station, in order not to interfere with others, must be kept strictly within an assigned bandwidth.

To secure bandwidth greater than that in the wire systems we have mentioned, engineers found the solution in microwave systems in which transcontinental distances are spanned by receiving, amplifying and retransmitting focused radio beams at intervals of 25 to 50 miles. By operating in the region of 6×10^9 cps, impressing the voices on the waves through frequency modulation instead of amplitude modulation, and by transmitting and receiving over separate beams at different frequencies, the system is able to accommodate 12,000 simultaneous conversations or voice channels.

What does the future hold? With transmission technology developing explosively and our inability to predict the inventions and discoveries which are just around the corner and which may radically alter the direction of development, we can only guess at the physical form of future systems that will be designed to carry huge amounts of traffic. Meanwhile, advanced transmission research engineers are looking in several directions—to new kinds of coaxials and radio systems as well as to the waveguide (a hollow tube) carrying extremely high frequency waves; they are also looking at laser beams.

Laser light, we noted, possesses the ability to travel considerable distances through "empty" space without serious energy attenuation. Although such a beam might be ideal for communication between ships in space, on earth there is the problem of the atmosphere. Light is scattered by mist and smog, and heavy rain or snow can completely blot it out. To operate a reliable day-and-night commercial system regardless of weather, it would be necessary to protect the beams, for example, by transmitting them through pipes filled with a nonabsorbing gas. However, pipe transmission involves its own peculiar difficulties; there is the basic problem of controlling the transmitted signal so that its information-bearing pattern is not seriously distorted. Prisms, lenses, and mirrors might be used to take the beams around corners or to follow the earth's contour, but it becomes a problem to keep the beams pointing in exactly the right direction despite the distortion of parts by thermal expansion and contraction or by lack of rigidity or exposure to shock and vibration. Transmission over long distances poses formidable engineering difficulties.

We also know that to apply light waves in a commercial system we must first develop a technology for modulators, amplifiers, filters, and all the other apparatus which is fundamental in any communications system. Little is now available. Here, too, arduous basic problems must first be solved.

If and when laser beams can be practically applied to their full carrying capacity, the prospects are spectacular. We do not have enough experimental data to predict reliably what percentage of the frequency —how wide a usable band—could be realized. Nevertheless, to form an idea, we might assume that a laser beam system could be designed to employ its available frequency as efficiently as is done in the microwave system previously mentioned. If we make this assumption, then, since the number of conversations or voice channels increases in proportion to the frequency, the number of conversations a laser system might carry comes out to be 800,000,000; this is more than four times the present population of the United States.

Even if it turns out to be a practical possibility, the simultaneous transmission of close to a billion voices over a laser beam is unlikely; the gigantic bandwidth can be put to other and far more likely uses.

Frequency bandwidth is like a dollar bill, which provides a specific amount of credit. You can spend a dollar bill in more than one way—to buy, let us say, a hundred 1-cent items or four 25-cent items. Signals have varying "prices" in terms of bandwidth. A TV program comes high-priced, with a 4,000,000-cps band—1,000 times as much as is needed for a voice. Thus, you can swap a thousand voices for one

TV picture. In place of a billion voices, a laser beam could send a million TV programs.

A TV picture, theory tells us, requires 1,000 times as much bandwidth because the information in a moving picture changes 1,000 times more rapidly than in a voice. Generally, communications engineers do not think of voices or TV pictures in assessing the potentiality of bandwidth. They think of a circuit as being able to transmit a specific number of "yes" or "no" bits of information per second. This, too, is the language of computers. Still it may well be that an age in which machines are taking over is destined to provide the laser with its great opportunity in communications. Much bandwidth is required to send digital pulses rapidly. Just as you can trade voices for TV pictures, so you can trade either or both for high-speed pulse transmission.

By accommodating high-speed pulse transmission, a laser beam offers an ideal path for communication between giant computers. The time may come when a computer on the east coast of the United States, having completed a series of massive calculations and "wishing" to communicate the facts to its mate on the west coast, would simply dial the appropriate number, then transmit a detailed account of the problems together with the answers through a system of pipe-enclosed laser beams in less time than it takes to wink an eye.

CAPSULE HISTORY OF THE MASER AND LASER

The idea of harnessing the orbital energy of atoms and molecules for useful amplification occurred independently to several workers in the microwave field, notably to C. H. Townes, then of Columbia University, to N. G. Basov and A. M. Prokhorov in the U.S.S.R., and to J. Weber of the University of Maryland. However, it was C. H. Townes who first saw how to make an actual device. In 1954 he built, in cooperation with J. P. Gordon and H. J. Zeiger, the first of all masers using ammonia gas and operating at microwave frequencies.

Subsequently, N. Bloembergen at Harvard University conceived and worked out in theory a maser amplifier using a paramagnetic crystal with three energy levels and capable of operating continuously.

199

1956   Applying Bloembergen's theory, H. E. D. Scovil constructed the first solid-state maser operating continuously (using the crystal salt lanthanium ethyl sulfate with gadolinium) at Bell Telephone Laboratories in cooperation with G. Feher and S. Seidel. Later, Scovil and others went on to develop the traveling-wave ruby microwave maser amplifier now used in reception of satellite signals.

1958   A. L. Schawlow of Bell Laboratories and C. H. Townes outlined the theory and proposed a structure for a laser (optical maser) to operate at light frequencies.

1960   H. Maiman of Hughes Corporation first demonstrated laser action using the visible red light of a synthetic ruby. The laser produced pulses only and could not operate continuously.

1961   A. Javan of Bell Laboratories proposed a laser employing helium-neon gas. He built one in cooperation with W. R. Bennett, Jr., and D. R. Herriott. Emitting infrared, it was the first laser to produce coherent light continuously.

1962   First continuous operation of a solid-state laser (using calcium tungstate containing trivalent neodymium) was announced by L. F. Johnson, G. D. Boyd, K. Nassau, and R. R. Soden of Bell Laboratories.

1962   A new class of lasers utilizing semiconductor junctions was reported almost simultaneously

by R. N. Hall, G. E. Fenner, J. D. Kingsley,
T. J. Soltys, and R. O. Carlson of the General
Electric Company; M. Nathan, W. P. Dumke,
G. Burns, F. H. Dill, and G. Lasher of the
International Business Machines Corporation;
and T. M. Quist, R. H. Rediker, R. J. Keyes,
W. E. Krag, B. Lax, A. L. McWhorter, and
H. J. Zeiger of Lincoln Laboratory of Massa-
chusetts Institute of Technology.

At this time—the end of 1963—nine years following the discovery of the maser principle and three
years after the first demonstration of laser action—
laser development still gathers momentum with no
slowdown in sight either in the development of the
device itself or in the exploration of its potentialities
for science and technology. At least 15 gases and vapors have been applied to produce over 220 different
wavelengths ranging from 5.9×10^{-5} centimeter in
the orange to 3.45×10^{-3} centimeter in the middle
infrared. Meanwhile some 15 crystals involving 13
types of doping materials (impurities) have been
harnessed to produce 40 wavelengths ranging from
6×10^{-5} centimeter in the red to 7×10^{-4} centimeter
in the infrared. In addition, laser action has been obtained in at least 6 semiconductors as well as in several
types of glass (crown, flint, and others) plus a number
of plastics and liquids.

INDEX

203